The Man Next To Me

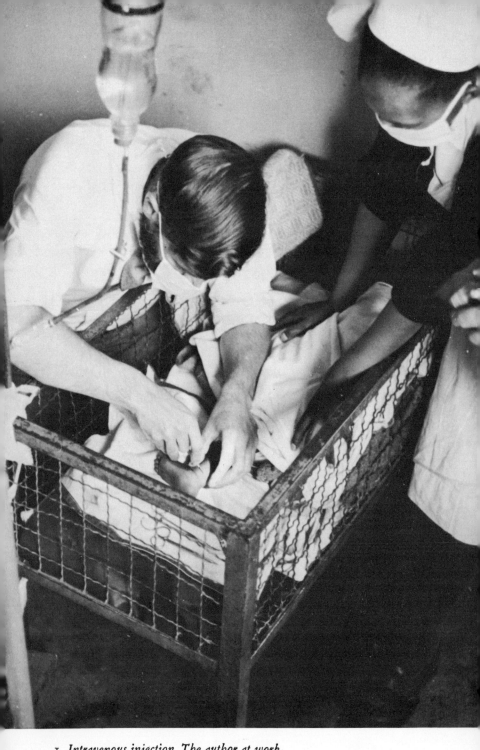

I. Intravenous injection. The author at work

The Man Next To Me

AN ADVENTURE IN AFRICAN MEDICAL PRACTICE

ANTHONY BARKER

HARPER & BROTHERS
PUBLISHERS   NEW YORK

FOR MAGGIE

Library of Congress catalog card number: 60-11768

PREFACE

THE mission hospital which is the scene of this book is set in a tribal reserve in Zululand. Such a reserve, where thousands of people are still living in the fashion of their fathers, is not a place where the great issues of South Africa are being decided. To find articulate, politically conscious Africans you must go elsewhere, to the townships and locations of the great cities, where the sting of Apartheid and political impotence is more sharply felt.

Yet the thatched homes widely scattered over the rolling grasslands, or nestling under the great sandstone cliffs of the hills, house men and women as individual as the inhabitants of Pimlico or Bloemfontein; whose lives are spent in the same struggles for food, enjoyment and love.

In South Africa, where racial taboos are entrenched by law into rigid social segregation of black and white, this human aspect of African life has been largely forgotten. More notice is taken of a man's racial group than of his person; as a non-European he is in danger of ceasing to exist as a human being at all. Perhaps it has always been easier to classify men than to love them.

But, however you view your fellow men—in a political way, or with the clinical eye of a doctor; with the yearning of a priest or the cold interest of an ethnologist—you have still, in the end, to live with them as your neighbours. This book tells of an attempt to restore this lost sense of neighbourliness. Both in purely professional relationships and in the more important business of learning to live together, in spite of the embarrassments imposed by custom, there has been a great deal to learn on both sides. The pitifully small harvest of fourteen years is gathered in these pages. For my own part, if anything good has been garnered, it owes more to what I have been taught than to what I have been able to teach; more to what I have received from these tough, humorous and astute people than to what I have been able to give.

I have to thank Anthony Sampson for tempting me, Robin Denniston for encouraging me, and my staff at the hospital, both black and white, for bearing with me during the long gestation and painful labour of this book.

ILLUSTRATIONS

1. Intravenous injection. The author at work *frontispiece*

2. Into Zululand *facing page* 16

3. Foundations of the Hospital 17

4. Explaining the X-ray 17

5. Doctor and friends 30

6. A cold little boy 31

7. Mother with rickety child 50

8. New arrivals 51

9. The sacrificial goat 74

10. Margaret Barker with patient 75

11. Mother and child 96

12. Mixing beer before the wedding 97

13. A nurses' tutorial 116

14. Young patients keep up with the news 117

15. Waiting outside the clinic 144

16. The mixture as before 145

17. Dancing 162

18. Peeling pumpkins 163

CONTENTS

PREFACE   *page* 7

1. *Mr Johnson's Hospital*   11
2. *Of Horses and Zulus*   24
3. *When My Man's Awd'*   34
4. *Shilling Doctor*   45
5. *They're all the same*   54
6. *A Web of Clinics*   61
7. *Boy with a Flute*   72
8. *Of Bricks and Water*   77
9. *Choose Your Own Cure*   88
10. *Surgery Against Odds*   100
11. *Magic and Mental Health*   111
12. *The Wheel Reconsidered*   122
13. *District Surgeon*   133
14. *The Dread Sickness*   141
15. *Little Stranger*   151
16. *Teacher or Taught?*   161

   The Self-Limiting Task   169
   Foreign Missions in the Twentieth Century

"A man must not choose his neighbour. He must take the neighbour that God sends him. . . . The neighbour is just the man who is next to you at the moment, the man with whom any business has brought you into contact."
—*George MacDonald*

CHAPTER ONE

Mr Johnson's Hospital

I

A S children we were taught to give regularly to the missionary work of the Church. Our sympathies were aroused by stories of the hungry, uncared-for children of foreign lands, enduring apparently endless suffering for which, it seemed to our childish thinking, the addition of the forbidding presence of a missionary was but cold comfort. We sniggered at our mental pictures of these agents of the Gospel, standing there under the burning sun, dressed in a uniform of cream Shantung silk, a topee covering greying hair, and strong, brown leather boots buttoning almost to the knees, as serviceable against the bites of poisonous reptiles as for the long day's march.

This unkind caricature was an extrapolation from a mental graph of missionary absurdity which began on a base line of wholly acceptable medical missionaries like Dr Livingstone, Schweitzer and Grenfell, and rose sharply to its last plotted point which was my Aunt Emma.

Which was not only arrogant; but also unfair, for Aunt Emma was not, nor ever had been, a missionary. She was, however, more than commonly religious, was devoted to The Cause, wore button boots, and boasted a tenuous connection with Robert Moffat, father-in-law of the great David Livingstone himself. Aunt Emma gave us Bibles for Christmas and, Congregationalists though we were, Prayer Books for our birthdays. Perhaps that gaunt, virtuous old soul gave us better gifts than we realized at the time.

My first real missionary acquaintance was the slight, tired father of a school-friend of my brothers. He had spent more than thirty years as a Baptist minister on the banks of the Congo, and had left behind him when he retired most of his small allocation of health. He had brought back a lifespan of memories, a permanently husky voice and a museum full of curios. The latter he housed in one room of an already tiny cottage high in the Cotswolds, he and his family sharing the rest of the house with a ubiquitous and deeply loved parrot. The museum was filled with exotic objects; the skin of a python, slave-whips of rhinocerous hide, masks, drums, beadwork, calabash utensils and distorted figures of human beings, with pointed breasts and trapdoors in their bellies like a Dali painting. The collection, which we were permitted to touch and even to play with, was the basis of a lasting impression. I wrote to the old man years later when Margaret and I were signed on for a five-year missionary contract, to tell him how deep that impact had been. In his reply I remember that he wished he could return to Africa, a sentiment it took us many years to learn to share.

2

On top of an already aroused interest in Africa which had developed from these schoolboy stimulations, it was meeting Margaret that finally compelled me to apply for at least one term of service as a mission doctor. Margaret was committed to serve the missionary society for a minimum of three years in return for their having financed her medical training. The prospect of three more years of separation at the end of a long romance which had begun by holding hands in the dissecting room, was altogether too much; I realized that the path to bliss lay not only through the church door—which was reasonable—but also up the impressive staircase of the Society for the Propagation of the Gospel. It also became clear that mental revision about Aunt Emma was an urgent matter; I made certain adjustments and married into a missionary career.

With the war already in its fourth year, the Society waived its normally inflexible rules against its candidates' marrying before fulfilling their obligations, provided that, on my release from the Merchant Service, I took on a three years' contract at one of their hospitals. We actually sailed a few weeks before the end of the war, our passage a gift from Alfred Holt's Blue Funnel Line, who rewarded my brief, undistinguished war-time service with them by signing us both on as crew of the *Antilochus*, I as surgeon, Margaret as surgeon's mate. The vessel was believed—such were the uncertainties of travel at that time—to be going to African ports.

On board we were treated like rare plants. The romantic souls of the sailors, whose pride was their toughness, peopled Zululand with gigantic savages, strewed the dusty veld with poisonous snakes and stuffed the rivers full of crocodiles. In vain we tried to suggest a less colourful picture; they considered our modesty becoming and made much of our dauntless courage. Even when we watched the weedy stevedores on Durban wharf at the end of the nine weeks' voyage, the sailors dismissed the evidence of their senses by saying that these were only town niggers, but up-country—where you're going, doc—you get the real big fellows.

Margaret's presence did something to both officers and men. Perhaps because they had been for so long separated from their wives; perhaps from some unexplained awakening of the chivalrous streak in us all, a gentleness settled over the ship which astonished everybody. Deck officers and engineers played rummy together for matches; Liverpool sailors let fall at worst an occasional 'damn.' When we finally left the ship there was a presentation from the men, the bo's'n making an imaginative speech, and flowers for Margaret from the officers who came down to watch the Zululand train pull out of Durban station. Having experience of other days, I was incredulous, but I was as bewitched as the rest of the crew during all that long voyage. The spell came off somewhere down the coast between Durban and Cape Town : 'Things are back to normal again,' wrote the Second Engineer, 'and the language is shocking.' The romantic period was over; both they and we were once again facing reality.

3

From the railway station to the hospital is forty miles. The arid, dusty road runs for the first thirty miles between the slack, ill-kempt barbed wire fences of European farms, with now and then a tin roof among the trees indicating a homestead, and now and then small groups of farm workers' huts. It is a rolling country, like the Cheviot, or—if such were possible to conceive—a rainless, unshrouded Scottish deer forest. Only when you cross the clanking girder bridge over the Buffalo River into Zululand itself can you sense an African atmosphere; huts increase in numbers; goats, cattle and sheep wander at will over the road and there are blanketed travellers driving pack-donkeys to the trading store, and knots of children dancing to school.

Yet it seemed difficult to believe that we were in Africa at all; for most of the way there had been only the back of the driver's neck to reassure us that this was a black man's continent. Even when we drove through the village and pulled up at the hospital, there seemed an incredible shortage of Zulus. We were warmly welcomed by a small group of the Doctor's friends, white ladies in floral cottons, who offered their friendship to us too, in all kindness, full of good will; but of black faces there were none.

Heaven knows what we had expected; perhaps rows of neat, cheering school children with gleaming smiles, delighted to see us; perhaps a crowd of sick men and women; cripples hobbling between primitive crutches; men with their legs bound up in old rags to hide the foulness of ulcers; the blind, lifting empty eyes, all waiting in hope for our coming? In our vanity, I fear we may have desired these things, but we did not get them.

When the door closed behind the Doctor, Margaret and I were left alone. Everything was still as a cathedral on a Monday morning; the half-smothered cooing of doves in the gum trees outside only enhanced the quiet of the little hut and increased within us the hollow sense of anticlimax. We had arrived; the romantic dreams of adolescence had frighteningly come to pass; everything to which we had looked forward during our long engagement was now realized. We had charge of a hospital in Zululand, even if it were only a rudimentary one, and the prospect terrified us.

All the events of that morning; the white railway officials, the long ride between the European farms, the kind ladies themselves, even, had somehow unnerved us. Set in the centre of a population of forty thousand Zulus we suddenly came to see that it might be difficult to meet them, let alone to get to know them. The final entry into the village had been worst of all; for it had proved monumentally ugly and not over-clean. True, this was at the end of the war and things have improved since then— or perhaps our standards have fallen—but on the day of our arrival the village was little more than a bungalow settlement of corrugated iron and naked cement blocks, grouped around the intersection of two sandy roads. Apart from the Government offices which were well built in natural stone, the rest was a higgledy-piggledy association of galvanized iron trading stores, hen coops, dead motor cars, squalid servants' quarters and, prominent at the cross roads, a tin public bar with a rusting roof. From this general air of dilapidation the hospital was not wholly free, in spite of gallant attempts to create a garden and the evidence of freshly-applied paint on the doors and windows.

Relief came with a knock on the door: 'There's an ambulance call come in; will one of you take it?'

It was a thoughtful act, for the Doctor must have guessed how we were feeling at that moment. 'Yes, I'd like to; what do we do?'

'I'll send the ambulance round to the front in a few moments,' she said.

That again was a good thing, because at that time I did not know how to drive a car and I was anxious not to parade all my weaknesses on the first day.

The ambulance, when it arrived, turned out to be a Ford delivery van, with a grandiose inscription on its panels and a faulty system of suspension. How many times in later months the central bolt broke which held the main spring and the body together, I cannot remember, but that day the ambulance behaved perfectly for the whole fifty miles of the journey.

Lucy Ndebele came in this way to be our first patient, on the strength of which she never failed afterwards to coax me into giving her free treatment. She was lying in darkness when I crept into the hut followed by the driver. 'What is the matter?' I asked. The driver interpreted for me : 'She says she has something wrong with her belly.'

I drew back the hard cotton blanket under which she was lying, and put my hand on her abdomen. There was an enormous lump which could easily be felt, arising out of the pelvis; it was tender and she winced under even the gentlest examination. I had not the faintest idea of what it was.

'I'm afraid this is rather serious,' I told the family. 'She should be admitted to hospital if you are willing for her to go?' The elders nodded : 'We want you to take her along.'

Relieved—for there was the hope that the correct diagnosis might be vouchsafed me on the way home, or at least that there Margaret might make up the breaches in my gynæcological knowledge—we bundled her into the cab of the ambulance and propped her up between us. She made the journey without a moan, but was as glad as I was when we had her safely tucked up in bed. At that time we had no sheets and were forced to nurse her between grey, weary-looking blankets in a small square ward with three or four other women. As soon as I could, I got Margaret down to come and see her, but even then the diagnosis remained a mystery. Ironically, our first case was difficult and obscure when so much seemed to hinge upon our making a success of it.

Fortunately, a few days of what we pompously called expectant treatment—and we had no facilities for a more direct assault upon the tumour—saw an improvement, and within ten days the lump had melted away under the kindly influence of the sulphonamide drugs we gave her.

Lucy was a success and we loved her accordingly : which is what doctors have done since doctors began.

4

Among the fighting men and military equipment made for nursery use by the firm of W. M. Brittain, it was still possible until a few years ago to buy Zulus. They were lanky little effigies, modelled in the running position, with spear, shield and fighting sticks ready for action against the less liberated likenesses of the red-coats. In our games their running had always been presumed to represent haste in the base action of fleeing but the reality had been otherwise in the Zulu war of 1879. To our new neighbours this war was a living memory, and men could still be found who could tell, through toothless gums, the story of the Sunday morning battle under the rocky hill of Isandhlwana and the all night assault on the garrison at Rorke's drift that followed it.

The causes of the war are not relevant to the history of the hospital. The final conquest of the Zulu military power and the deposition of their king were of the usual stuff of empire, half greedy, half altruistic, achieving much in some spheres, and settling nothing in others. Following the time honoured path of imperial government, Sir Theophilus Shepstone replaced the Zulu king, Cetshwayo, and broke down his unified kingdom into thirteen separate principalities under the leadership of men as diverse as John Dunn and Hlubi Molife. Dunn was a white man assimilated into Zulu society who had taken to himself the number of wives appropriate to a minor chieftain. From these he had established a dynasty of Dunns, whose descendants still people the coastal strip of Zululand.

Hlubi Molife—who was the kinglet over our own area of Zululand— was a Sutho who had shown his loyalty to the Crown in the war and was rewarded for his services by a grant of land along the Buffalo River. He and his followers, with their wives and children, their goats and cattle, came down from the mountain country of Basutoland and formed, between the white farmers of Natal and the marauding Zulus, a buffer state ten miles broad. Hlubi's people considered themselves a cut above the rabble of defeated Zulus and, if housing and the domestic arts are anything to go by, they had some reason for the good conceit they had of themselves. They built in stone; comparatively roomy houses with windows and built-in cupboards and shelves of clay, decorating their homes inside and out with ochres and natural earth pigments from the mountain. They held to their own customs and, as is so often the way with minorities, remained self-consciously aloof from their neighbours.

It was Hlubi who asked the young Charles Johnson to come as a teacher to his people. Johnson had been a transport rider during the war, but when

2. *Into Zululand*

3. *Foundations of the Hospital*

4. *Explaining the X-ray*

the fighting was over, had been content to stay on in the barren upland country of the Zulus. He went to Hlubi's people as a teacher, but after a while took Holy Orders to equip himself for the wider vocation of building up an indigenous church which should ultimately spread to the less receptive Zulus. Much of this was realized within his lifetime, and the memory of his bearded countenance, his frock coat and stern manner, lives in the minds of the older clergy. 'I worked under Johnson,' Fr. Mbatha told me one day when he was convalescing at the hospital, 'he was a very strict man, but afterwards, if he had been sharp with you, he always came and said he was sorry.'

It was impossible for Johnson in the '80s to avoid a degree of responsibility for the bodies as well as the souls of his flock. Toothache is a great leveller and, in common with early missionaries of all persuasions, Johnson became an expert puller of teeth. The agonizing services he rendered his converts must be appreciated against the background of domiciliary dentistry as it was practised at the time. There, a nail, or even the point of a spear, was insinuated between the teeth and the carious offender levered out. The missionary's torment, the sharp iron taste of the forceps and the scalding red suction of the dying tooth, was better if only because of briefer duration. If the word of a later Bishop of Zululand is to be believed, not all of Archdeacon Johnson's extractions were successful. This bishop claimed to have surpassed Johnson's total, and with his accumulated experience felt justified in making a modest charge for his services; one shilling for an easy tooth, two shillings if difficulty were encountered, and half a crown for removing the stumps left behind by the archdeacon.

Children wasted by malnutrition and young women in needless peril of childbirth, must have presented a poignant challenge to the archdeacon's limited skills. There was no doctor who could assist when simple remedies failed, nearer than the market town of Dundee, and that was all of thirty miles of horse-drawn jolting from the mission. It must have tried his faith almost past endurance to offer ghostly consolations to women who, under the hand of a skilled obstetrician, might yet have lived to see the years pass and their children grown to usefulness. But there was no help except that which he could offer.

It was left to Johnson's successor, A. W. Lee, to establish medical work in that part of the country. Lee was assistant priest under Archdeacon Johnson and later stepped into his gaiters, ultimately becoming Bishop of Zululand. He was faced with the same problems of needless suffering and felt the same dissatisfaction at his own unskilled efforts at its relief. Being an impetuous man, he started a hospital at S. Augustine's mission station in memory of Charles Johnson. Many must have shaken their heads over his folly, for folly it was to open even a rudimentary hospital with little or no money at all. But Albert William Lee was a man in whom enthusiasm and fluency of speech combined to dazzle the eyes of the cautious and stop the mouths of the critical. He obtained money from sere lawyers and cheered on the already awakened enthusiasm of the District Surgeon, Dr Bessarabia. Two rooms in the mission buildings were his wards; one Zulu nurse, Sanna Mbatha, his staff; there were at first no patients.

Yet within a few years this embryonic hospital, scarcely recognizable as such to eyes accustomed to the tiles, the plate and the polish of a modern hospital, had begun to make its mark in the district. Maternity work brought the women, but for years the men remained retiring, preferring to observe from a reasonable distance the effects of the hospital's ways on their womenfolk. The women brought their children once they had themselves experienced relief and the men, cautiously at first, then with increasing boldness, came ultimately to accept treatment for their own ailments.

Lee read the signs of the times aright when, a few years later and for the purchase price of £1,200, he bought an unused trading store in the magisterial centre twelve miles from his mission and moved his hospital to where, in the centre of the village, it could serve a wider population. In every way it was a wise migration, bringing the hospital to the District Surgeon's doorstep and to the confluence of three bus routes. Under the hand of our predecessor the hospital had grown both in buildings and in influence so that we were given a small but living unit to take over on our arrival.

5

We also inherited a staff. Edith Tett, the Matron, was our senior at the hospital by six months, most of which she had spent in the shadows with a near-fatal attack of typhoid fever. This had been a contribution from the hospital cook who had risen from a sick-bed herself before being fully recovered from an undiagnosed fever, with a zeal for work in excess of her knowledge of hygiene. Within a month of her coming, the Matron was complaining of headaches and, as her temperature rose, she slipped into unconsciousness and muttering delirium. She had just returned from sick-leave when we came, and for the rest of her five year contract, until her marriage in 1950, she never missed another day from illness.

Jabajaba Zulu was the sanitary man who, in those far-off days, emptied buckets into a trench at a decent night hour and by day tended the two head of cattle which were our herd. In appearance he resembled a Bushman, being short of stature and having a large head. His mouth was enormous, fringed with widely spaced teeth arching over an outsize tongue which gave him an almost cretinous look. He was bronchial, asthmatic and kindly, spending on sweets and oranges for the children in hospital what little of his wages his mother left him after her monthly visits.

Jabajaba's care of the cattle was limited to an affection for them coupled with a singular lack of knowledge of their needs. Each evening he drove them—and with them went an attendant host of buzzing flies—across the hospital grounds from the commonage to the cow byre. He was baptized about a year after we arrived, receiving the name Philip, but I never heard him called by that name by any of his friends, who preferred the onomatopœic title of his unregenerate life. He died of heart failure in 1947.

The driver, Amon Mlambo, who managed the ambulance work and also drove the Doctor on her midday visits to her friends in the village, was from a family with a long Christian tradition dating back to pioneer missionary days. His father, who died an exceedingly old man some years before our arrival, was among those who had fought in the Zulu war, and had been present at the defeat of the British forces at Isandhlwana. The Zulu soldiers had appreciated the valour and determination of that small, hopelessly outnumbered force facing death under the mountain; they also knew that the Imperial troops were issued with a powerful medicine before battle which made them fight like tigers. For this medicine, once they had occupied the British lines, they sought eagerly. They found the kerosene and ignored the rum, and learned that the effect of lamp-oil, at least on an empty stomach, is, far from producing courage, to give rise to terrible nausea and final collapse. There were a number of possible loopholes in this story which is perhaps to be remembered more for its poetic justice than for any well-documented truth it contains.

Mlambo was the first of an over-long succession of dispenser-drivers, none of whom has yet served so faithfully or so well as he. He was a believer in rescinding the laws preventing Africans from obtaining spirits and frequently demonstrated the inefficacy of those laws to stop any one possessed of sufficient determination from getting all he needed. He taught me to drive, for war-time restrictions on the use of petrol had precluded my learning in England; he also gave me my first lessons in Zulu. After six years he left to marry and better himself, but his three children have all been born at the hospital, and he remains an infrequent but welcome visitor.

There were, to complete the number of our staff, six student nurses in training, to the best of the hospital's rather limited capacity, for the ultimate goal of a Hospital Certificate of Nursing. In 1945 there was no training available for women of less than School Certificate standard. A singularly stuffy Nursing Council refused for many years to recognize the establishment of an Enrolled Assistant Nurse grade, in spite of its obvious application to a country of low general literacy and in spite of the proven worth of this grade of nurse in hospitals in other countries. Each hospital which took, for vocational training, young women of a lower educational standard than School Certificate—and in the country it was seldom that we had sufficient applications from girls of even that standard—could do no more than issue its own certificate, so that the qualifications were uneven from centre to centre. Fortunately the Provincial Government of Natal took the law into its own hands and regularized the training of Assistant Nurses, recognizing that many of these young women made up in vocational sense what they lacked in general education. By 1957, Provincial Nurses, as they came to be called, had so vindicated their training that the Nursing Council was compelled to accord to them some measure of grudging recognition.

But for the six original nurses there was less hope of achieving any status at all. They worked hard, and we conscientiously taught them, but matrons of town hospitals were frequently rude and often brutally discouraging to the nurses when they later applied for even the humbler kinds of work. 'You're not trained at all' they would sniff at our nurses at the end of their four years' course. Weeping, our Rose-Janes, Clarices and Mimis would return to us with sore hearts: 'What shall we do, Matron?' They usually did find work in the end, and many were highly spoken of, but the unbridled power of matrons of the baser sort was able to inflict smashing blows on the assurance and happiness of our trainees.

Nursing's double demand for knowledge on the one hand and dedication and kindness on the other has made an absolute standard of training impossible anywhere. This is even more evident in countries without universal education, where there are, for every child who reaches even the modest standard of the General Certificate of Education, a hundred who fall by the way and as many again who have never sat in a classroom in their lives.

There is an élite of the less than fully successful, and from this élite we drew our trainees; from girls who for family reasons, lack of money, loss of parents or failure in the larger Nursing Council schools, had been unable to finish what they had set out to do. Many proved difficult to teach up to the relatively high standard of the Provincial examinations; some failed to grasp the ethics of the thing, never achieving that nice combination of firmness and kindness that was needed; a small but steady proportion got into trouble, became pregnant and were suspended for a year or more in consequence; the best did very well indeed, and came to be our loved and trusted staff nurses and, more rarely, sisters. More and more we came to rely upon these young women; increasingly they rose to their growing responsibilities. In spite of dark days, the training of nurses remained one of the hospital's more permanent achievements.

The six nurses made no complaint of their hard conditions and accepted their few shillings reward with becoming grace. We strove not to abuse this wonderful willingness, but it was hard not to do so when there was so little money to go round. They were cheerful—almost painfully so— and sang at their work, sometimes in Zulu, but more often a penetrating rendering of 'Tiptoe though the Tulips' and other songs of the 'thirties which had just reached Zululand after a ten-year journey through the tropics. Their home was an uninspired, rectangular building with a leaking annexe in the form of a pent house at the back. There was no plaster on the walls, which bared their cement bones, unadorned even by whitewash. Because there was no ceiling you could look up into the corrugated iron of the roof which, discoloured by soot, muttered and creaked to itself in captive paroxysms of expansion and contraction with the daily course of the sun. When, two years later, we cleared out this wretched house and saw our nurses more fitly accommodated in a new home, we came across mouldering heaps of corn-cobs and furtive squirrel-stores of sulphonamide tablets; symbols perhaps of that yearning for private possessions in those who are compelled to live publicly—the same urge that fills the soldier's pocket book with old theatre tickets, locks of hair and faded photographs of father in his allotment.

6

Lastly, apart from the seven patients who, on that May day, were the inmates of the wards, we inherited two cattle and a proportionate share in a pig. A pitiful yield of milk from the two cows persuaded us, even if the precipitated filth of their daily journey to and from their grazing ground had not already done so, that they were more trouble than they were worth. We felt—the process of our humiliation had as yet hardly begun—that we should set an example if we were to keep beasts at all; an example that others might see and emulate even in so humble a corner as the shippon. Since, also, neither of us knew anything whatever about the management of a herd, we decided quite soon to have the creatures destroyed and to feed thē patients and ourselves on the meat. I went to see the Sergeant who was a close and friendly neighbour, and asked him for his help in their slaughter.

Sarah was to be the first victim, a cow whose right eye was a sightless, bluish dome. With less noise than I had shrinkingly expected, the Sergeant's heavy pistol ended Sarah's days and she slipped with a warm, hay-laden sigh into death. I was just thanking the Sergeant while he put away his gun, when we both saw a quiver in the dead cow's flank. We looked at each other in horror : 'Doctor, man, she's in calf!' he groaned.

'Quick, a knife! Run and get a knife from the Matron!' I shouted at the cowman, who tore off gibbering towards the house, returning almost at once with a carving knife. Margaret came running down at the same time, breathless and anxious. Our first Cæsarean section was accomplished in a moment, and the calf—which was, of course, a heifer—survived its premature birth just long enough to vouchsafe a few mucous gurgles in derision of my folly and then lay dead, couched against its mother's cooling flank.

I think the Sergeant took it even harder than we did; he was an Afrikaner of country stock and, according to his people's traditional cattle lore, should have known better. But the shame was ours also; we had received obstetrical teaching from the lips of two of England's finest practitioners and it had failed us utterly in the hour of decision. It was an ill-omen and we left the scene of our downfall with sinking hearts.

Even with the pig things went little better. Sweet and pink, it occupied a small sty behind the now deserted cow stalls. It was the Matron's pet and fed richly on the kitchen scraps, reaching in a short time a size suitable for slaughter. But sentiment marches ill with husbandry and the Matron could not bring herself to have it killed, having grown fond of it. It grew large enough in the end to be unable to get about at all, but for which fact it would have escaped when its vast bulk pushed over the wall of its sty. Matron was persuaded to have it put away then, and we planned a splendid pork dinner for the staff and patients. I was to do the cutting up, with Margaret as assistant, the carcass having been suspended from the beams of the verandah roof by wires through its hind legs. The knife sank deep into the plateau of the pig's back but, manly though that sweep was, it did not even reach down to the vertebrae. I cut again, exposing bone at a depth of four inches and with a saw cut the soft, unathletic bones, dividing the animal into two. We separated the limbs from the trunk, and cut the chops as neatly as we could. The least portions were enveloped in folds of blubber, the flesh being represented by whisps of pink muscle itself infiltrated by the all-pervading greasiness. The flensing took two hours and every casserole and jam tin, pan and biscuit box in the hospital became our try-pot. Our hair and everything about us oozed the clear, warm oil for that night and for days afterwards. The meat was only just sufficient for our small company, but we were spared the necessity for buying any cooking fat for a good while to come.

CHAPTER TWO

Of Horses and Zulus

I

NATHANIEL NTULI shot himself a few hundred yards outside the hospital. His suicide was a premeditated act, but he nevertheless died an hour or two before he had intended and with one last job undone.

He was a big man, stout, breathless, wheezy, already a little worn by the years, yet still tough under an outer coating of fat. A Zulu of a former day and generation who still had sufficient education to give him insight and detachment and to make him very good company. He was employed by the Department of Health for the control of malaria, the vaccination of the district's children and the detection of cases of leprosy. It was in connection with these patients that I first knew him, for, among my duties as a young man newly arrived in Zululand, was the examination of doubtful cases of the disease and, in accordance with the law of the land, the commission of those found to be infected to a special hospital on the coast.

Where Ntuli and I differed was that he knew the disease in all its manifold disguises, whereas I had never seen a case in my life. What is more, I suspect Ntuli knew perfectly well that this was the case, although he was far too well-mannered to say so.

In reward for his work the Health Department paid him a salary which, though not large, more or less provided for his children in their short passage between birth and premature death. Some, however, of his numerous children managed to survive to school-going age, and for these he borrowed money successfully from a number of traders and government servants to send them to the mission school near his home. He also borrowed occasionally from me.

But, as with most of us, Ntuli's income never did much better than trail along behind his expenditure like a dispirited dog, and he remained among the honest poor.

The Devil entered the story in the elegantly dressed form of a fellow Health-Assistant by the name of Mnareng. Perhaps it needs two to enter into any shady compact and certainly some of the blame must be put on Ntuli, but had there been no Mnareng the sum of Ntuli's loans would by now be fairly large and I should still count myself rewarded to exchange the time of the day with him on the road outside the hospital. Mnareng was an accomplished sheep-stealer and knew how to obtain sufficient bootleg brandy to satisfy even Ntuli's splendid thirst. Together they investigated reports of new cases of leprosy; together they sprayed stagnant water with paraffin to choke mosquito larvae; together they coveted their neighbours' sheep, and together they stole them.

The police quickly learnt what was going on and came unpleasantly near to looking over the wall of Ntuli's sheepfold. To a man of Ntuli's understanding it was evident that the end was not far away. With jail and ruin a certainty and his children's future in danger, he decided there was just one thing he wanted to do before he lost his freedom and his job—to kill Mnareng. From his army days he had a service revolver hidden in the thatch of his house, a treasured illegal memento of his time in Egypt and Libya. Under the bed, in a cardboard suitcase, he had a treasured, illegal bottle of brandy; with the one for execution and the other for courage he left his home. Perhaps it was as well that informers told the police where he was going, his greatcoat pockets bulging, for murder is an ugly crime however great the provocation. They closed in on the bus he had boarded to take him to Mnareng's home.

Ntuli saw the constables coming and bolted. He ran, fast and frightened, down the stony slope towards his home valley. Once he turned and flung the bottle of brandy at the nearest constable, but it did him no good and they gained on him at last on younger feet than his. He did not turn round again as the distance shortened between him and his pursuers. When they were close enough for him to hear their panting and the squeaking of their boots on the rocks, he raised the gun and, still running, with his face towards his home, towards everything he cared about, he blew his brains out.

Two days later his wife came to see us. She carried an envelope in her hand which she gave me, making a little curtsy as she offered it; 'This is for you, doctor,' she said, 'my husband left it for you.'

I had forgotten that I had lent Ntuli five pounds only a month or so before at the beginning of the new school year and for a moment could not imagine what these clean, new pound notes meant.

'I think he owed it to you,' Mrs Ntuli explained.

I stood with them in my hand, wondering if I dared be sentimental and give them back; it was certain she would need them now if ever she had needed money, but the lady anticipated me: 'There are others,' she said proudly. 'He told me to sell two oxen when he was gone and pay all his debts; I know he wanted you to have your money back.'

I took the money then and, because this is not a fairy story, I spent it.

2

Ntuli taught me to recognize leprosy by bringing cases up to the hospital and more or less rubbing my nose in the clinical picture. Later, and with the experience of many cases seen and followed up, it seems remarkable how slow and inept a pupil I must have been. I suppose I was looking for the Biblical leper, 'White as snow,' although it is doubtful if leprosy as we know it to-day occurred in Biblical times at all. My old Chief, Mr B. T. Rose, whose phenomenal knowledge of the scriptures was left to him as the waters of a strict upbringing receded, used to contend that Naaman's leprosy was probably nothing worse than the scabies which was relieved by the sulphurous waters of Jordan, where the prophet had told him to go and bathe. The fact that the deceitful Gehazi caught the disease off him in so short a time becomes rather less surprising if this was the case.

Leprosy is transmitted by a specific germ and must therefore be considered an infectious disease. But it is not easily caught, and in nearly every new case there is evidence of long-continued association with a known sufferer. Its main effects are on the skin and in nervous tissue; there are also moderate constitutional symptoms, mild fever, malaise and loss of weight. The skin changes include a coppery rash on the trunk and neck, and a coarsening of the face which leads in the end to that leonine appearance which put Holmes on to the correct explanation of the face at the window.

The results of the invasion of the nervous system—and the bacillus seems to be highly selective in which nerve trunks it will attack—are more permanent. The nerve fibres to the hands and feet, both those serving the function of voluntary power and those conducting sensation upwards to the brain, are damaged and lose their power of conduction. The extremities become partially paralysed and wholly insensitive. Minor injuries, cigarette burns, abrasions from ill-fitting sandals, are not noticed at the time and may become heavily infected before the patient is aware that anything is wrong. The combination of muscular paralysis and loss of sensation leads, unless great care is taken, to the partial or complete loss of fingers and toes. It is this secondary result of nerve damage, rather than the actual disease process itself, that leads to the disfigurements that have given to leprosy its reputation for horror.

From their ancient association with uncleanness, the words leprosy and leper are being dropped from medical and scientific writings, and the disorder referred to eponymously as Hansen's disease after the Norwegian discoverer of the bacillus. Slowly, too, in some countries more rapidly than in others, the stigmata of infection are passing; treatment, which has nowadays become more effective in arresting the progress of the disease, has also become more humane. In South Africa it is still obligatory to segregate the sufferers in special hospitals, but that for Zululand is a happy enough place and an increasing number of men and women are willing to go there without coercion and with reasonable expectation of discharge within a year. Thereafter their follow-up examinations are the responsibility of the district surgeon and the health assistants.

3

Slow as I was to learn Ntuli's lessons in the recognition of leprosy, I proved slower still in my response to his efforts to teach me horseriding. I have never shared the enthusiasm that young women from good homes reserve for the horse. In my experience the animal is at once capricious, treacherous, moody, too big, sycophantic and uncomfortable to ride; but my duties were occasionally to demand long journeys to inaccessible places where, since walking was out of the question and a bicycle impracticable, I was compelled to use the mount that Ntuli brought me.

Soon after our arrival I was asked by my retiring predecessor to go with Ntuli to investigate a doubtful case of Hansen's disease. The patient's home was in the wild valleys in the southern part of the district and I accepted cheerfully as much because I wanted to see the countryside as from a desire to see any patient whatever at such enormous trouble. I knew further that the Doctor's knees gave her trouble, so that if mine could do some vicarious flexing for hers, again I was content.

June in the Southern hemisphere is deep winter; a time of night frosts and days of blue and gold which can be warm enough and are invariably bone-dry. You may wake to ice on the pond's edge and dress in woollen expectancy of penetrating cold, but by mid-morning the sun is in control of the day and remains master until the time of a refrigerated evening star.

Ntuli was only a few minutes late with the horses at the rendezvous. He rode up on his white mare, leading the horse whose reputation for gentleness was the principal reason for its choice for my use. He got down from the saddle and held the correct stirrup by which I was to mount. He must have known that I had never been on a horse before, because he placed his body so that I could only face the right way and put the proper foot in the stirrup; but he could not help the fear rising in my mind at the combination of my height above the ground and the crowding memories of bolting horses and necks broken in the hunting field which were my heritage from books read in the security of arm chairs or the nirvana of my bed. There was, in truth, no cause for alarm for the creature stood perfectly still and failed to answer to the invitation to gee up. Possibly the horse only understood Zulu, or the bite of a switch on its rump, but it looked as if it understood everything very well indeed, so that Ntuli's sadly uttered comment—'She knows that the doctor does not ride horses'—had a true ring about it.

Ntuli gently took the reins from my too tight grasp, passed them over the horses head, and attached them to his saddle. We moved off like a continental tramcar and trailer, I relieved at least from worrying about where we were going, which left me free to turn my whole attention to staying in the saddle. I was determined not to hold on, and for the most part maintained that determination; only later on, when darkness had fallen and I had graduated to holding the reins, did I find my hand reaching down to caress the saddle.

With Ntuli leading it was possible to enjoy the view, an uninterrupted sweep of more than fifty miles on every hand. We were to travel south, in the general direction of the confluence of the Buffalo River with the Tugela, a meeting of brown waters in a far blue valley. From where we began our descent from the mountain could be seen rank on rank of hazy hills, pointed, jagged, eroded but all revealing their common origin by the successive horizontal strata of their deposition. The high country of Zululand is like that; laid down in layers of sandstone and then eroded into innumerable hills, fissured by watercourses and deep river valleys. In the low country to the east of the escarpment the slopes are green, soft and feminine, but towards the Drakensberg their outline becomes harder and there is evidence of volcanic intrusion in slopes scattered with red-brown boulders of weathered dolerite and, in the valleys, veins of pink quartz.

We began the descent into the first valley. The track was steep as a boarding-house staircase and the horse took the descent uneasily, its back tilted forwards and downwards in sympathy with the hill-side. It had not occurred to me that this would happen and I wondered whether saddle and rider together would not slowly move forward relative to the horse. When the gradient became too sharp we dismounted and led our horses, to my secret content.

Under the mountain the shale-strewn floor of the valley exhaled the sun's warmth. Everything lay quiet as a velvet cushion in the heat. We got on again, Ntuli leading in a fast trot which turned, without any prompting from me, into a canter. It was a rollicking movement, stilling my fear and restoring my self-respect in momentary exhilaration. It was the funfare sensation all over again, the horrified delight of the big dipper, the sensuousness of the roundabout. Approaching the river we slowed down, the horses' confident feet broke rhythm and went into a high-heeled mincing gait, shaking us terribly for a moment until a more sedate walking pace brought peace at the last.

With a heave the horses climbed the far bank and for the first time I began to understand the wonderful muscularity, hard and controlled, that horses hide beneath satin skins.

'The doctor learns,' murmured Ntuli.

'Learns what?' I asked, touchily.

'The last doctor I brought over this river fell off the back of his horse here' was all the encouragement I got; we continued in silence.

4

That silence was the first of many which have plagued me in my attempts to make light conversation while walking along innumerable roads with many African guides. An African house-surgeon tried to explain the feeling to me one night when, tired out, we were walking together back to the hospital after leaving the ambulance, broken down, in some sodden ditch. Suddenly at the end of about ten minutes' walking without saying anything, he asked, 'What are you thinking about?' Caught out in a mental vacuum, I rather shamefacedly replied that I was not really thinking of anything at all. 'That's what happens when you walk too much of the time' he pronounced severely. 'You have to walk too much if you are an African.' Later on, I was often to be reminded of what he had said when, driving along country roads, I had to hoot Africans off the bumpers whose minds were elsewhere as mine was that night.

When we reached the home after raw hours in the saddle—for my progress had been painfully slow—it was to be met by a pack of baying dogs of individual and grotesque breeds. They came at us, yelping and slavering, liver-coloured and brindled, with pale yellow eyes and mangy tails, followed by the cries of all in the home: 'Get back! I'll beat you! Be off!' in shrill chorus, addressed, I hoped, rather to the dogs than ourselves. The mongrels withdrew, cowering under the hide whip of the young man who was evidently sent to welcome us. Cringing, unbelievably thin and broken in spirit, they fawned upon the tyrant youth, licking the hand which held the instrument of their oppression, with no more eyes for us at all.

The young man watched as we dismounted, and took no notice of my idiotic 'Good morning.' Then, just as if there had been no crescendo of barking and snapping, no shouting, no oaths and cursing, he said quite gently, 'I see you, friends.'

Ntuli replied, 'Yes, we see you.' A pause, then from the youth the unalterable next move in the game: 'Are you all well at your place?'

'Yes, we are well; we ask after your home and people.'

'No, we too are well, but we are sick.'

'We have come to see your sick person . . .'

The courtesies pass to and fro, punctilious and always collective in their application. The whole family greets the family of the strangers; the individual is not raised above his people.

The woman we had travelled so far to see was sitting with her back to the first hut in the enclosure and paid us no attention at all. She was about thirty years old, short of stature and well-covered. About her hips she wore the pleated leather kilt of a married woman, dark, greasy and decent; an equally greasy but not so picturesque T shirt covered the upper part of her body and over her shoulders was pinned a red woollen blanket. Her hair was done up into an inverted cone, wider at the top than where it started over the crown and back of her head, kept in shape by being interwoven with string. The whole headdress was smeared with red clay except where a string bandeau, chalk-white, broke the continuity between the hair and the rich chocolate-brown of her oiled forehead. Queen Nefertiti, I remembered from the *Children's Encyclopædia,* had done her hair like this. Knowing the tradition of the Zulus that they came down from the North, it was tempting to wonder if this young woman was not still sharing an inspiration of a court hairdresser of nearly four thousand years ago?

Her illness was apparent; a vast leg, swollen to twice the diameter of the opposite limb, and certainly not leprous. She indifferently declined any treatment, which was a relief in that for her, at that place, I could have done nothing which could have benefited her at all, and we left

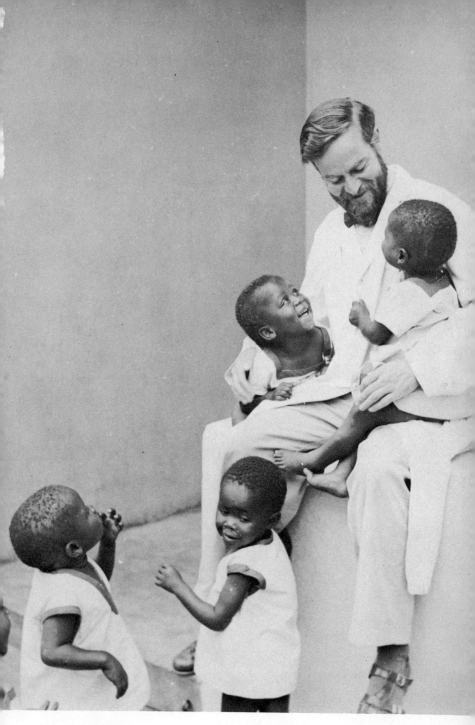

5. *Doctor and friends*

6. *A cold little boy*

after a short rest in the shade. No one offered us drink or food; but then, no one had asked us to come either. We were outsiders, spies for the Government and I at least was incurably white. It was a valuable reminder in the first week of a missionary career that you would be taken on your merits; if you waited long enough and worked hard enough you might later be accepted.

Our way back took us past the home of Phineas Sithole, the chief, whose older brother's widow had been forewarned of our coming and invited us in to eat at the chief's house. Gratefully we accepted, but the curried fowl served whole on my plate was for the white doctor alone; once she had set it before me, Mrs Sithole left me, nor would Ntuli hear of joining me though by now he must have been as hungry as I was. My scruples were assuaged easily enough; I ate enormously and with relish the meat, dumplings and gravy. Getting up from the table I could see Ntuli through the half-open door; his face was buried in an earthenware pot which he held cupped in his two hands. His throat undulated as he gulped at the thick, sour beer it contained. He was happy and wanted to share his pleasure. 'Come and meet the chief' he belched as I showed myself.

Chief Sithole was sitting under a tree at the other end of the compound. He was of the old tradition of chieftainship, regal in manner almost to the point of arrogance and reputed to have eleven wives. He had wanted his brother's widow, my hostess, to come into his family when her husband had died, to 'enter' his home as a wife, in accordance with the Zulu custom of providing for widows in a polygamous society, but Mrs Sithole has refused as a Christian to accept the union, and thus preserved her son's right of succession to the chieftainship, a position he later came to hold.

He greeted me very civilly, and through Ntuli I gave him greeting back again. He inquired after my family and home and all the formal courtesies were concluded before the temptation of my presence overcame his good manners. 'Will the doctor examine me? Has he his instruments with him?'

'Tell the chief I should be pleased to examine him.'

Ntuli interpreted at some length: 'The chief says he has pains here'— Ntuli dug me sharply in my loins with his thumb—'and here,' placing an open hand gently over his own lower abdomen.

The chief settled back on his stool, his eyes closed, expectant.

'Ask the chief to expose his chest, please,' I requested, and a little stir went through the watchers. He took off his cotton vest, exposing an enormous chest. A cry of awe and a shy burst of clapping from his followers greeted the sight of his gross body thus bared for examination. He had well developed breasts and the fat over his shoulders and under his hairless armpits lay in ridges, divided by deep horizontal grooves. I put my stethoscope to his chest wall, but heard nothing but the slight murmur of the afternoon wind and the stirring of the leaves of the tree under which we were gathered.

'Breathe!' I commanded.

The flesh heaved, the shoulders rose and fell; from his nostrils the chief produced sighings and whistlings, but not a thing could I hear through the earpieces.

'Breathe deeply!' I coaxed. 'Deeper still.'

I tried again but there was no evidence of any air entering his lungs at all. I looked at my stethoscope; could it be that I had a punctured tube? No, everything seemed all right and yet nothing reached my ears but the whisper of the breeze and the extraneous noises from the old man's nose. Panic began to take over the consultation; I prodded at the abdominal wall and punched the broad back, but still diagnostic silence reigned absolute. Sweating, I looked again at his round face, beardless save for a set of drumdreary whiskers over his cheek bones, and envied him the smile of seraphic complacency that he had worn ever since the examination began. Then, quite suddenly, I saw the whole thing; this failure of mine to hear anything did not matter; my ignorance didn't matter; for this was not a medical consultation at all, but a game of make believe. I was the doctor and a guest; he was the chief and as the chief should be examined. Symptoms were mere words, the examination a pantomime played out according to inflexible rules, the result should be a prescription at least and, preferably, an injection at the end.

I was to meet this pattern again and again, but on this first and important occasion it was a discovery which released me from the bondage of panic and gave my solemn words an assurance which, on the slight evidence of my examination, they should never have had.

'I am glad to say,' I told Ntuli, 'that the chief's condition is in no way serious; I shall be happy to send him a bottle of medicine on my return to the hospital.'

Ntuli leant close to my ear: 'The chief will expect an injection,' he whispered. I made the decision of my life: 'Please further tell the chief that I do not think an injection will be necessary.'

Ntuli said no more, but interpreted my opinion to the chief without enthusiasm.

Of Horses and Zulus

The practice of giving injections to African patients, irrespective of the merits of the case, is widespread. 'They expect it,' runs the argument, 'and if I don't give them one, somebody else will,' which up to a point is quite true. An injection of vitamin B might, furthermore, do good, for many are malnourished and, if the patient's heart is set on an injection, the very act of giving one will increase confidence and help in his restoration to health. Certainly such injections do no harm to the patient, but it has seemed to me the first step on the slippery path for the doctor, to be avoided by those who would keep their disciplines clearly before them, and more especially by the missionary practitioner who is in any case pledged to quixotic attitudes.

However that may be, the chief took my words in good part, thanked me most kindly and said good-bye. Two days afterwards I sent him a bottle of Mist. *Soda Bic cum Rhei,* that sandy remedy of our childhood colics, and he lived in good health until his sudden death a few years later.

It was quite dark when we reached the top of the hill again. By that time I was long past caring for the niceties of horsemanship and was never so pleased to see the treacherous Chevrolet that was to take me home again. Ntuli stabled the horses at the headman's home, said good-bye to me and settled to a comfortable evening over the beer pots, relaxed in the cheerful company of his fellows, to whom I was then, and have remained only too regrettably ever since, a foreigner.

CHAPTER THREE

When My Man's Awa'

I

EVERY morning of the week, Sundays excepted, if you are up early enough to be present when the sun leaps over the golden mine dumps, you can watch the Natal train arrive at Johannesburgh station. Do not concern yourself too much with the rear of the train, reserved for white passengers; watch the front coaches.

From these, before the train has quite finished its journey, the black travellers begin to pour on to the platform. First come the city men, experienced visitors in neat brown suits and broad brimmed hats. With their leather brief cases they might have come from some dark Wimbledon or Motspur Park. Thoroughly at home, they move with neat-shod feet towards the correct exit—the one marked Non-Europeans—and pass away up the stairs to mix with the crowd hurrying citywards over the bridge.

Countrymen, newcomers to the city, take longer to descend. They travel like nineteenth century immigrants with baggy umbrellas and their dear possessions in bundles and heavily-corded cartons. The women, who are in the minority, are mostly sober, respectable wives visiting their husbands long away, or mothers searching for sons who have never written. They wear their black skirts long and decent and cover their hair with quiet-coloured cloths. Here and there a woman is dressed in the scarlet tunic of a full member of the Bantu Methodist Church; rarely among the crowd appears a tribal headdress, modestly swathed in mutton-cloth. But most of the passengers are men, house-servants returning from leave, garden-boys, caddies, porters, cooks, waiters and clerks in no great hurry to reach their place of employment. They stand awhile in groups, talking to old acquaintances, laughing with new friends made in the few cramped hours of travel, easy, brothers in the colour of their skins, allies in subordination.

Here are the young men, laughing, shouting, striding down the platform, their lilting steps betraying their country origin as surely as the coloured discs of wood which they wear in their stretched ear-lobes. Some are wrapped in blankets, others wear seedy jackets and ragged trousers;

most have, for decoration, a yellow duster round their heads or tied below the knee. About their necks are beadwork ornaments and love tokens given them as a keepsake by their sweethearts and lovers. The young men are quickly rounded up and fall in behind the agent of the recruiting organization who, with his peaked cap and martial air, is sergeant-major to this bucolic army. He marches them away, still joking, still excited and noisy, across the road and up Eloff Street, threading their way between pedestrians, dodging the traffic, until the whole colourful crocodile loses itself at the unfashionable end of the great thoroughfare.

The Lords of the Mines saw them come and were glad, for labour was scarce. Sophisticated Africans, city-born or city-conditioned, had long since ceased accepting underground employment; they knew there was better pay, more freedom from the clogging paternalism of the Mine Compound, as well as greater safety in the expanding secondary industries of the Witwatersrand. To recruit labour for the hewing and bearing of the thousands of tons of rock needed at the extracting mills, meant throwing the net ever wider, beyond the cities, farther than the country towns and the Reserve Territories, even beyond the borders of the Union itself. Upon these precious youths, with the smoke of dung fires still clinging to their blankets, the nation's economy depended. Only for so long as they arrived, worked and went home again could the digging for gold be economically accomplished.

The artisans saw them come and were disturbed. Raw boys to-day, unskilled, unambitious except to escape the stagnation of tribal life, how long would it take them to learn the dexterity of tradesmen? How long before they made organized demands for more money, better living accommodation, more responsibility? The day might come when these black youths would take over the white man's work—their work—and command the high wages for which former generations of tradesmen had suffered and fought. Fearing these things and forgetting that the black man, too, was a fellow working-man, they entrenched their skills as white prerogatives and looked coldly upon the aspirations of these strangers.

The men of the Government saw them come and were well-disposed. The coming and going of migratory labour suited the Government very well. It solved the problems of housing, urbanization and segregation all on a single day. These young men had come to the city, not to settle and ape the white man's ways, demanding rights and privileges; they were here for a useful job, contracted for a number of shifts underground and returnable, like empty beer bottles, at the close of their contract. Returnable to the Reserves where, the politicians said, they belonged; returnable to their own way of life. It was regrettable that this meant the temporary breaking up of families—it was even hoped that, in future, industries might be developed on the borders of the Reserves to reduce the scale of the migration—but, because the politicians were realists, they saw this as inevitable and, finally, in the country's best interests.

So the coming and going went on. It was necessary for the gold-mining industry that it should; it was also necessary for the labourers themselves, for to them, work in the cities was the only hope of keeping themselves and their families in health and reasonable comfort.

It had not always been so, for there was a time when a man could farm his own land and graze his stock in expectation of providing, by the efforts of his labour, food and the material wants of his family. Even when his lands had become exhausted there were always more beyond the horizon. But that wasteful, semi-nomadic life had passed for ever with the conquest of the black kingdoms and the settlement of white farmers. From thenceforth Africans were owners of their own fields only within the reserve territories, and the reserves represented only thirteen per cent of the country's total area.

The population grew even as the soil, over-worked and ill-fed, failed in its fertility. Year by year men's labour yielded them a little less; year by year the hungry storms of summer and the roaring winds of early spring ate away the land, gnawing gullies out of the maize fields and blowing away the fine rich topsoil. The herds, no longer free to extend their pastures, grazed and grazed again over the same acres, so that the sweet grasses never seeded themselves, but died out, leaving only the poorer varieties on which no beast will feed.

With the increasing need not only for food but for money with which to pay taxes and buy the things that a man could no longer produce for himself, someone from the family was compelled to accept service for a cash wage. A little work could be obtained locally, but only a little, for the majority work meant the work of the mines, and on the mines there was no settled labour; always a man must go, do his stint, and return.

The way to the mines is through the office of the Native Recruiting Corporation, an organization with agents in the magisterial districts throughout the Reserves. The office in the village is of red brick, a neat round hut against whose wall is propped a monstrous, grinning effigy of a black miner, his breeches decorated with bright patches, a helmet on his head, his arms akimbo. Along the road outside the office a notice board invites :

> Lovers of cattle! Lovers of money!
> Here is the easy way to the City of Gold!
> Here is the office!

Money, gold, adventure, uniformity; these are irresistible to the youths who loaf, slack shouldered, by the trading store, molesting the girls and crowing with salacious laughter. They sign on, glad to cut adrift from the boredom of home, glad to identify themselves with others who wear the helmet and the patched trousers of the cardboard giant outside the office. They go away boys and come back men; as a beginning, a spell in the mines has perhaps all those advantages and disadvantages which fireside men beyond military age claim for a period in the army.

It is a different matter when, a few years later, a man is married and is compelled to go away for months or years together. Then, what was adventurous in adolescence becomes the recurrent stress of parting and exile, with all hope gone of a stable home life or a chaste and decent marriage. Yet for the men at least, absence has come to be looked upon as almost a normal pattern of life. Soldiers have always sloughed off much that is disagreeable, anxious and wearisome in their home lives when they don uniform and march away to the wars. It is always the women who have suffered because their capacity for self-deception is never so highly developed as that of their husbands. To them, the loneliness and loss of present affection is unmitigated by the masculine consolations of conformity, of being a man among men. And for the Zulu wives, lovers and mothers, who have few other ways of expressing their loving natures save in the physical processes of reproduction, the burden of their men's absence is doubly hard to bear. Out of the chill prospect of almost continual separation is born an inescapable need for the satisfactions of frequent and repeated childbirth, drawn out by suckling into months of full, warm, affectionate living.

Even if these needs are met by the husband's leaving behind him on his return to work a new, embryonic life moving in the black silence of the womb, there is still fear for the mother; for how long will this precious life be hers to cherish and to work for? All too soon the birth, and from infancy to the time of separation is a very short while.

2

Mrs Shabalala lost her first baby after an exhausting labour at home. In bitter loneliness of spirit she had lain on the floor of the hut, reinforcing the expulsive efforts of her tired body by hauling on the hide rope slung from the roof. Snug in their blankets, the old women who were watching her took snuff and compared the force and frequency of Mrs Shabalala's contractions with those that had accompanied the delivery of their own children, now grown up and gone. It was the cowardly, they affirmed, nodding together in agreement, who had long labours.

When at last the baby had been spilled out on the earth floor, it had lain quite still, deceptively pink in death.

Both Mrs Shabalala and her husband were agreed that the next delivery should take place in hospital, and she was scrupulous in her attendance at antenatal clinic. She was seasonably rewarded by the birth of a fine, live boy.

'A splendid little chap!' Margaret's voice was brisk as a fishmonger's.

'Eight pounds if an ounce!' exulted the midwife.

But there was no response at all from the other end of the bed and the two women looked across at each other for a moment before bending towards their patient.

'Whatever's the matter now?' they asked, seeing the tears shining in Mrs Shabalala's eyes. 'Is something wrong?'

The sluices opened in a spate of tears. 'No, no, nothing's wrong. It's only that I had so wanted a girl. Now I've got a boy and he'll leave me so soon, and I'll never see him again, ever.'

'But you've got him now,' Margaret soothed. 'Look, here, take him in your arms : he's all yours now.' And she settled the young migrant in the crook of his mother's arm.

Thus it is that a husband's every leave becomes a loving struggle against the capriciousness of human fertility. To be pregnant is to have months of emotional satisfaction ahead; to fail is both a misery and, all too often in the eyes of gossiping neighbours, a disgrace. I used in my ignorance to laugh at the mournful bride of three weeks whose body urged upon her unaccepting mind the realization that she was not pregnant. 'Wait, wait!' I would blandly reassure her, 'You'll become pregnant soon enough, don't you worry!'-And she would smile kindly, knowing that I had not understood that her husband was due next week to return to work. Later, we learned to take this urgency more seriously, although, at that stage there was precious little we could do about it, except to understand her need, be kind and express our impotent pity by giving her a bottle of iron mixture, green and astringent, as a sort of love potion.

Most of the men come home for the ploughing season in October and stay until after Christmas. In that brief season—and the time is, for many, much shorter—has to be packed passion enough for a year of separation. The successful couples come smirking into the clinic. 'Want to know if you are pregnant?' you ask after the first two or three hundred times. And usually it is far too early to say. 'Come again in a month's time, and I can be sure.'

But the chances are that you will not be the first to tell her at all. The diviners and prophet-priests of the innumerable African sects that have sprouted about the Church's trunk, will use their fey arts to go one jump ahead of the doctor. It is only a pity that they are so often wrong, breeding false hopes where long deferment has already sickened the heart. But because pregnancy is a common condition, they are also frequently correct, and the doctor's caution is taken as further evidence of the limitations of his calling.

Unsuccessful couples, whose tree must bear no fruit, suffer sorely. So unacceptable is the realization of her barrenness to the unhappy woman that her mind and body often conspire together to deceive each other, suppressing her bodily functions, swelling her belly and providing a full accompaniment to the false pregnancy in the form of self-appreciated 'fœtal' movements. In time the chain snaps and the body takes over its inexorable mastery, leaving a mind drained of hope, and emotions dulled by despair. Less often the pseudocyesis goes on to spurious labour, a catastrophe of abdominal pains with no visible result : the stage is set for the great performance, the minor actors are in their places, the audience hushed and expectant; only the principal actor fails to appear, for he does not even exist.

News of Mrs Magubane's labour reached me through the police sergeant. Not uncommonly information of this sort comes out when Europeans, no more indiscreet than their fellows, discuss the private affairs of Africans; for privacy is for the better-to-do of society, and those who have to do without many things must do without that as well. It appeared that Mrs Magubane had had her baby in the night and murdered it; certainly the baby could not be found next morning, but neither could the place in the floor of the house where she was believed to have buried its body. We went to investigate. The woman sat in tears, resentful of our intrusion on her misery. 'Where is your baby, Mrs Magubane?' I asked as kindly as I could. But there was no reply and I tried again : 'May I see the baby, mother?' But her stillness became more still and her ears even less receptive to my questions. After a while I obtained her passive assent to examination, and the infanticide was resolved. There was no case, for there was no corpse; no corpse because there had been no birth; no birth because there had been no pregnancy. I left the small, dark hut conscious of the proud, solitary grief which I had enhanced by being an official busybody.

3

Upon the migrant labourer in his pilgrimage from the decayed security of tribal ways to the distant, desired life of the city, is placed a great burden. Society loads him with the duty of creating its wealth and rewards him with very little for it. His family asks at his hands its many needs which he must try to satisfy at the same time as he is making his own, personal living. Nor is his family a meanly-conceived group of father, mother and the children, but an expanded, cohesive unit in which a man's cousins are his brothers, his aunts his mothers, and where he may have to bury more grandmothers than it is reasonable for any man to possess. Each member may have claims upon his sparse earnings, and to these claims he usually responds cheerfully and with as much material help as it is in his power to give. Even while observing these duties to his family he has to find a way to lay by sufficient wealth for his lobolo when the time comes for him to marry.

Lobolo is the European dowry in reverse; it is the responsibility of the intending bridegroom to hand over to his parents-in-law, eleven head of cattle, or the equivalent in cash, before or at the time of marriage. Yet, though the groom gives and the father takes, this is neither a purchase nor a deal between individuals. It is a family act; a token of good faith; an insurance against the risks of human mutability and the inconstancy of marriage. Implied is a guarantee of satisfaction, with both bride and beasts returnable under certain clearly defined conditions. It is, perhaps, less than perfect, but it is morally and practically a world in advance of the widespread promiscuity which follows upon its breakdown.

The homes which shelter the extended family, with all its ramifications among the living and its uneasy awareness of the ever-present dead, are groups of huts under the governance of the head man of the family. There are no villages, nor is there any close association with neighbours for common protection against danger or for mutual assistance in the daily work of the fields. Men prefer to withdraw among their own kin when the day is over.

Although several families may draw water from the same spring and share common grazing grounds for their herds, the homes are built as far apart as possible. It is a mode of living resistant to the formation of a public opinion, which has perhaps made the hospital's task a little more difficult in its efforts to introduce better infant feeding, safer obstetrics and preventive inoculation. It also gives the head of the family powers which a dictator might envy; he may, if he is disposed to be helpful, insist on a member of his family having treatment in hospital when ill; he may equally forbid the performance of a life-saving operation on one of his dependents. In his absence, women are often afraid to make up their own minds in moments of crisis; telegrams must pass to and from his place of work, with a consequent delay which may prove fatal.

Nor are the living the sole inhabitants of the family home. One year after his death, a man's spirit is invited to return to the house which was his in his lifetime, the invitation being the responsibility of his descendants. It is a ghostly restoration at which all the living members of the family must, so far as is possible, be present.

The belief in the power of the Old People, the ancestors of the clan, to reach out of the shades and control the lives of those members still in the world, increases the already strong family-sense. Leading to respect for the elders and obedience to their rulings, it has many aspects which are good and cohesive in a society only too liable to fission. Yet, since the clan's life is considered to be so much under the influence of outside forces, there develops a destroying fatalism which cripples the will to act decisively in times of adversity. This is more than ever true when sickness attacks the home; where disease is considered to be inflicted by these arbitrary ghosts, angered by a man's misconduct or by the magic of his enemies, sacrificial propitiation is the first line of defence, precious time being spent in consultation with diviners and magicians that were better, perhaps, used in reaching medical help.

4

It is clearly desirable that the dead should be buried, if at all possible, within the confines of the family home. When Sihawu Shange died after years of breathless cyanosis, his sons pulled down part of the wall of the cattle enclosure and buried him there, rebuilding the stone wall over his grave so that the old man remained in death no less a feature of his home than he had been during his lifetime.

For those who die away from home, in hospital or at work in the great cities no expense is spared to return the body to the family home.

Nurse Winifred caught typhoid fever from a patient through a failure on her own part to carry out the prescribed precautions against infection.

Her parents lived 250 miles away, and the message was delayed in reaching them, so that she was almost well again by the time her mother came to see her. The mother was a formidable woman, a schoolteacher, imposingly dressed in a neat costume and a hat with a heavy brown veil.

'I must take my daughter away at once.'

'I don't think that is necessary at all, Mrs Sikosana.' Margaret's manner was reassuring. 'She's almost better now and was up for the first time yesterday.'

But no blandishments deflected Mrs Sikosana's firm purpose : 'I want her to-day, if you please; I have ordered a taxi.'

'But why do you want to do this when your daughter is almost better?'

'She still might die, and I want her nearer home. If she dies here it will cost me a hundred pounds to get her body back home.'

Understanding broke on Margaret. 'And you mean the fare, alive, is only three pounds?'

The logic was overwhelming and so was the evident saving in hard cash. We temporized, and a few days later Nurse Winifred went on sick leave from which she did not return. There was no question of her dying then, but she took up nursing nearer her home to avoid the hazard of such expenses in the future.

Death in childbirth, undelivered, precludes peace for the spirit after death, and means for the woman an infinite extension of her birth pangs to the very limits of time. One hot Saturday afternoon the ambulance was called for a difficult maternity case, but returned with the news of the mother's death shortly before the arrival of the ambulance. The nurse in charge of the case reported that the mother had died before the baby's shoulders were delivered, and she had not interfered, but come away leaving everything as it was. It was regrettable, but it was an all-too-familiar tale and I dismissed it a little too easily from my mind.

The next morning, which was a gold-and-black one hot enough to silence even the weaver-birds' chatter in the trees, saw a deputation of men ride up to the hospital. They were wearing wide-brimmed hats and heavy overcoats, despite the sun's heat; the sweat trickled from their noses and chins as if, not unexpectedly, they were melting away. The oldest of the men greeted me; he was the father of the dead girl of yesterday's tragic parturition, and wanted to ask me something. I made the conventional expressions of sorrow which he gravely acknowledged. He cleared his throat : 'There is something we want to ask you.' He looked for support from his fellows, and went on, 'Will the doctor please help us?'

'I don't see what I can do at this time; what do you want me to do?'

'We want your help.' He found it difficult to approach the point and looked again at his friends. 'We want you to deliver the woman.'

'But she's already dead, isn't she?'

'Yes, doctor, but please, we ask the doctor to do this thing.'

It was Sunday and very hot. I looked for a loophole of escape from the thirty-five mile journey that I should have to make if I accepted their request. What was the use, anyhow? I went down to see Sister Zulu in the maternity ward.

'What ought I to do, Sister?' I asked when I had explained the position.

'You should go, of course,' was her emphatic answer, given without a moment's hesitation. After that I had no way out, and went.

It was high noon when I reached the home and walked, shadowless, past the group of silent women sitting unmoving on one side of the compound. I did not greet them and they gave no sign of recognition as the father took me over to the hut where the dead woman lay. Before I went in, I asked him if I had permission to cut the child's body if it was necessary in order to deliver it. He hated saying yes, but he did so, adding that if I could manage the delivery without damaging the child's body, it would be much better. I promised my best and entered the hut alone.

In the darkness I could make out a blanket strung between two roof poles in the manner of a screen, behind which was the lumpy, blanket-wrapped form of the dead woman. Her knees were still flexed in a last, expulsive effort. I knelt on the floor and by the light of the little paraffin wick which had been left burning by her body, extracted the child with the greatest possible ease. To have delivered the woman safely and happily the day before could have been no more difficult than this macabre performance; her death was useless and unnecessary, a sacrifice to ignorance and indecision.

'I've finished,' I told the waiting men as I crept out of the low entrance on my hands and knees, 'and I didn't have to do anything.'

More than all I wanted to get away from all this grief. As the gears of the ambulance engaged, the women suddenly began keening, throwing themselves on the ground in paroxysms of misery; beating their breasts; pounding their heads with the palms of their hands, wailing and shriek-ing in a symphony of despair. Who had decreed the storing up of these wild emotions while the women sat dumb beside the huts? At what signal had they been released? Was one the conventional expression of the other, or was this perhaps the natural sequence of sorrow, from silence to mourning? Were all these spurting tears, these sobs, really an act of rebellion against the cruelty of a fate which had cut off a young life at the moment of its perpetuation? Certainly I had nothing to say to them, and was glad when the noise of the engine and the increasing distance stilled the sound of the women's wailing on the hot afternoon air.

CHAPTER FOUR

Shilling Doctor

I

THERE was an air of the wild West about the old trading store which Bishop Lee purchased for his hospital. Sheriffs might have lounged under the lowering verandah, chewing and spitting, and iron-tyred mule-carts ground the rough dust of the road beyond. Its corrugated roof was supported on concrete pillars, precast by an engineering firm on the coast with more thought for their durability than respect for any of the classical styles of Mediterranean architecture. The columns had apparently been obtainable in even numbers only, so that, when the seven which supported the verandah roof were all in place, the eighth was set up in the garden near the doctor's hut. There it remained, a monolith of unknown function for almost five years until Margaret and I, returning one night from a supper engagement, pushed it over and ended its symbolic days.

From the verandah a double door led into a narrow passage, flanked by flimsy ceiling board which divided it from the empty male ward on the right and the out-patient department on the left. Both these rooms were badly lighted by a single window and a small skylight apiece; both had two doors upon which they depended for ventilation; both were unspeakably stuffy on still days and torn by freezing draughts when the wind blew.

On Wednesday afternoons the out-patient room was stripped of its movable furniture and scrubbed out to do duty as an operating theatre. For this purpose it could hardly have been less suited, with its crumbling mud-plaster and its decaying wooden floor-boards, but there was no other room with even the slight qualifications it did possess, and the surgical problems we faced at the beginning were, mercifully, simple ones. No one suffered as a result of its use and the wound infections and septicæmia which unsympathetic observers might reasonably have prophesied did not occur; but, then, we took no needless risks and moved as soon as we were able to a more hygienic environment.

Because there was no money—the total grant from the Government at

45

that time was £150 a year—all the furniture had been home-made, frugally compounded out of kerosene boxes nailed together to make serviceable shelves and cupboards, with the addition of planks secured at the corners for legs. The Ancients, whose floors were as uneven as were the floors of the hospital, knew very well that a three-legged stool will stand stably anywhere you place it, but the lesson has been lost in more recent times. Pride, and a certain stiffness of mind, had decreed that all our cupboards should have four legs, with the result that each stood in precarious balance with at least a hymn-book and often half a brick under one or more of the legs to restore stability. The cupboards were painted a serviceable, permanent green.

We shared the building with a pale, unseen garrison of white ants and a more noisy army of rats. If you sat very still at a time when all work was done for the day and the out-patients had gone home with their bottles and ointments, it was possible just to hear the jaws of the white ants eating away the window frames as they worked in their dark tunnels, undaunted by the huge task of eating even so small a hospital as ours. The rats, lusty in love, noisy in the endless hunt for food, scampered and squealed night-long in the ceiling. From above us they descended by the water pipes to make free of our food stores and ascended again, carrying the soap from the bathroom to sustain their young.

When it rained moderately the roof leaked in a controlled way through screw holes grown wide with rust; by moving beds and placing bowls it was possible to ensure that nobody got wet. But when the hail came pounding, heaping against the decayed guttering and filling the valleys of the roof, the melting ice formed dams against the escaping water and the whole building became sodden and cheerless. If any one was to remain in even the limited comfort that we were able to provide for our patients, we had to climb up on the roof and shovel the stuff away.

Behind the store building was a rough field, thick with grass and dominated by two mutilated wattle trees, under one of which stood a pile of broken bedsteads, rusting iron-ware, paraffin tins and leaking chamber-pots. Between the wattles and through a small orchard of barren plum trees, ran a ditch carrying kitchen waste water and much else besides from the hospital to a square pond at the bottom of the grounds. Here, in the black, bubbling waters of the pool, frogs bellowed and croaked in an anthem of ecstasy through the warm spring nights of their mating.

There was also a kitchen, a laundry with open-air washing tanks and a piped water supply of its own, and an agreeable little block, originally built for an operating theatre and sterilizing room, but used as maternity and women's wards. Its rooms were small, square and unpainted, but the floors were good, there was plenty of window space, and the little wards had a clean and decent air about them. Here lay our original seven patients, of whom the undisputed queens were Lephina and Saraphina, two old ladies smelling strongly of cod liver oil. They were suffering from the same skin disorder and, bandaged or exposed, almost exactly resembled each other. Retaining her cheerfulness in spite of the terrifying appearance of these two ancients, was ten-year-old Truth, an engaging little girl with a deranged hip joint; Lucy Ndebele and three other blanket-clad figures made up the complement.

2

The humble buildings and the small number of patients were evidence of the problems, which would unquestionably be ours, of making any effective contact with the patients. In our self-confidence we were less daunted by these difficulties than we should have been. We had read of the crowds besieging the dispensaries of India; we knew about Schweitzer's deliberately simple hospital at Lambarene and we believed that we should have little difficulty in attracting the needy to our wards. We set to work; I built cots from our packing cases, Margaret sewed mattresses and stuffed them with hay. We waited, but for a time that seemed to our vanity unending, there was little increase in attendance. It seemed that most of our patients were content enough with the traditional ways, thinking it unlikely that white men could comprehend black men's sicknesses. Those who used medical services at all were sophisticated enough to go to private doctors in the cities or to the long-established mission hospital in the market town thirty-two miles away, seeing only too clearly that we had but little to offer. Hurt, we watched this exodus of potential patients leave by the morning bus, and were glad to treat the crazed, the very elderly and the poor who began, slowly, to come to us. Every patient was a treasure, an investment in the golden future; we examined each with exemplary thoroughness and treated those who came like dukes. Later, when the exodus turned again and the migration was towards the hospital rather than away from it, we tried to retain these standards against the onslaughts of fatigue and familiarity.

But at first we were grateful for the humblest tasks which we were asked to perform. Not long after our arrival a man came up to the out-patients with a cat under his arm. 'It's been run over and can't walk,' he explained.

I looked at the cat; its back was broken and the outlook hopeless. 'You ought to have it put away.'

'Yes, I thought so myself; will you destroy it for me, please?'

The request, I felt, would have been more properly made to a veterinary surgeon or at the knacker's yard, and I was about to refuse with dignity when it occurred to me that I really had nothing else to do at that moment, and I ought not to decline to perform the last offices for a suffering creature. I closed the lid of the lethal chamber on the silent form of the chloroformed cat with an executioner's sense of a job well done.

3

From our first morning in the out-patient department it became clear that there was no room for specialization. Among the coughs and minor ailments of that day was a woman nursing under her petticoats an enormous abdominal tumour. Big though the tumour was it could almost certainly be removed to her lasting benefit, but at that stage the operation was beyond both the hospital's facilities and my own surgical skill. Together, Margaret and I went to ask our predecessor what was her policy under the circumstances.

We were away perhaps ten minutes, but returned to find the couch empty and the patient mysteriously disappeared. We called her name, but there was no answer; we asked the other patients what had become of her, but they sat woodenly, repeating that they did not know at all, for they had heard nothing and seen no one pass out of the room. We looked up and down the road, but she had completely vanished, nor did we ever see her or hear of her again. It was unlikely that we were the first doctors who had examined her, and I fancy she was looking for a medical man who would grant her a bottle of medicine or an injection rather than advise a dreaded operation. If so, she must have seen in my eyes the mixture of satisfaction and suppressed excitement with which, for all their dissimulation, young surgeons view large tumours. Knowing from that moment what the sentence would be, she had made her escape while there was yet time.

From the lower abdomen we swung our attention to a decaying tooth which required extraction. While I was at sea I had pulled out one or two teeth, more or less successfully, from Chinese members of the ship's company. With Oriental sagacity the Chinese firemen were said to send to any new surgeon who boarded the ship the junior member of their community to have one of his teeth extracted. If the tooth was pulled without excessive pain and came out whole and unbroken, others more senior would come to the surgery for relief. But if the pilot-patient reported unfavourably, the firemen would nurse their decayed stumps in the fo'c'sle, with the help of opium fumes, until port—and a dentist—was reached. Margaret had not even my limited experience, which constituted me as surgeon-dentist to the forty thousand people of the district.

This ranging from the field of the gynæcologist to the confines of the dentist, paying tribute in passing to the knowledge of the physician and the dexterity of the surgeon, has been the pattern which, established on that first day, has been followed ever since. It is a world away from the contemporary trend towards the limitation of disciplines in the interests of their more perfect mastery and, while it has evident advantages in enabling the doctor to see his patient as a whole, it also carries with it a small but inescapable penalty of death and disablement from incomplete knowledge and inexpert management.

Ben Zungu helps to keep me humble. He had the misfortune to break and dislocate his ankle in such a way that the small bones of the foot were driven up between the separated leg-bones. Had I known a little more, or had I at that time possessed greater skill, I should have screwed the fragments into a stable relationship. Instead I set the ankle and put the leg in plaster more in hope than in knowledgeable expectation, thankful that the whole mass of swollen, deranged tissue was decently covered by an elegant white casing. It was a brave attempt, but Zungu developed a plaster sore and we had to remove the cast after a few days, which gave the foot its chance to assume the position in which it came ultimately to rest, turned through eighty degrees and one and a half inches shorter than its fellow. Surprisingly, he can walk on this terrible member and comes regularly to clinic, profuse in his thanks for my work, beginning his loud benedictions while still limping into the room in full view of all the other waiting patients. Mendaciously I reinforce his unreasonable satisfaction at this deplorable result, saying how pleased I am that we did not have to amputate the leg; which only increases the warmth of his greeting, and, less pleasing to myself, the frequency of his visits.

Our failures were not numerous, but they lay in the wards as a permanent accusation of which we were uncomfortably reminded as we did our rounds each morning. There are always failures in any practice, if failure is the right word to describe those incomplete answers to impossible medical and surgical questions. There are patients whose condition does not

permit of total relief, or even of more than the slightest degree of pallia-
tion, who are forced to spend long periods of time in convalescent homes
and hospitals catering for the chronic sick and disabled. For our patients
there was no such special accommodation and their continuing presence
in the wards was a stern reminder of the great deal that medicine—even
medicine at its best—cannot accomplish. It might even be salutory for
some physicians and all surgeons to keep a few beds for the chronic sick
in their teaching wards.

4

I was shocked on that first morning to find that the Doctor levied a
small fee for her services, for it had never occurred to me that any one
would be expected to pay for treatment at a mission hospital. Years as a
student, followed by a few month's residence in hospital where money,
if it was talked about at all, was a matter for clerks in basement offices,
had reinforced a childish view of money which is not uncommon among
university graduates. Entering general practice, at least in the days before
the National Health Service, the young doctor's financial puritanism
suffered a bruising from which he had to recover rapidly or starve; which
was unpleasant, but it was the way the world went. With experience and
growing maturity, he learned to charge fairly and, when need arose, to
remit his fees charitably.

No one, in any case, had ever heard of a free or contributory medical
service and certainly Zulu patients expected to pay something for their
treatment. It was less a matter of whether or not a charge should be made
than of how much it was reasonable to demand. There are two schools of
thought; those who, like ourselves, have tried to find a fee which is
within the capacity of the humblest to pay and yet is consistent with professional dignity; and those who hold that any supposed poverty among
Africans is the product of craft and humbug, and that, if you but know
where to find it, each family has its hidden crock of gold. 'They're not
poor,' runs the argument. 'Hell, I wish I had as many pound notes hidden
away as some of them have got.' The latter school is also convinced that a
large fee carries implications of medical superiority; 'Charge them up,
man,' the advice goes on, 'they'll think you a much better doctor if you do,
especially if you give them an injection.' Politely we acknowledge this
often-repeated counsel; obstinately we have declined to act upon it.

Yet it is as true in Zululand as elsewhere that prestige is gained by
paying heavily for medical advice. The wiseacres are often right in their

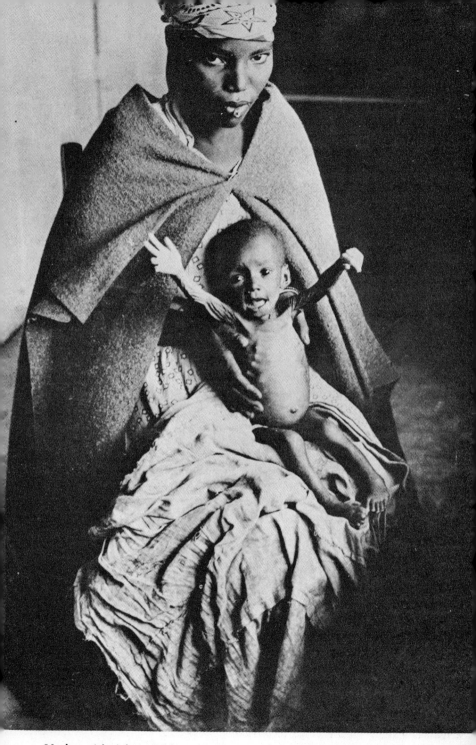

7. *Mother with rickety child*

8. *New arrivals*

estimation of the value patients set upon a large fee, but the really poor are necessarily more numerous than those who can afford the luxury article, and to the poor we were especially committed.

Some time after we had mastered enough of the language to understand more or less what was being said, we went to matins at a mission church. The preacher was the catechist, poor as only catechists are poor, and the theme of his sermon was the untrustworthiness of princes and the eternal reliability of God. He illustrated his points by several scathing and accurate comments upon men and institutions who would have considered their services, had they been asked their opinion, as primarily charitable and benevolent. 'Look at the doctors!' he demanded. 'What do they ask you when you go to see them? How are you feeling? How is your pain to-day? No! They say'—he parodied the dreadful Zulu of the white housewife—'where is the money? That's what they say!' And I knew then, if I was not aware of it before, that there will always be a tension in paying for the doctor; a fine line between justice and exploitation.

Our predecessor's method of charging was the reasonable one followed in former times in English practice, of making an assessment of the patient's means and charging him accordingly. The Robin Hood principle was applied of ensuring that the fat merchants paid for the jolly peasants. If it had a defect, it was the difficulty of knowing, on the part of the patient, whether he was to be treated as a fat merchant or a jolly peasant, so that we sometimes came upon women standing beyond the hospital fence in an agony of indecision. 'How much is it to see the doctor?' they asked when you went to their rescue.

Our initial unease about charging has persisted, even though we have tried to reduce apprehension by the introduction of a standard charge of a shilling for each attendance after an initial registration fee of half a crown for a new patient. Without this money we should be many hundreds of pounds poorer every year which would represent a serious hole in the hospital's budget. With it we reduce some of the utterly frivolous demands on our resources and, at the same time, we find a small charge to be a remarkable comfort to the doctor who makes it, while securing to the patient the right to call his doctor a fool.

Within the bounds of charity we have been strict about the payment of these shillings, too strict sometimes, I believe, yet not without the intention of spotting need when it was real. So often, after a half-bantering argument, the shilling has been cheerfully enough brought out of a hat or from the knotted corner of a petticoat, that it would be easy to fall into thinking of Africans as animated banks who can be persuaded to disgorge money for the benefit of their European benefactors.

We made no extra charges as a rule, but occasionally sought to recover some of the expenses of X-ray plates until we learnt the unfairness of this from an old lady whom I had asked to come up to the hospital for an X-ray of her chest. The lung fields were clear, and I reassured her, murmuring that the fee was half a crown. She declined to pay, reminding me with respectful but impeccable logic that nobody had benefited by the examination but myself as, for her part, she could not read the picture, while if I, in my imperfect knowledge, needed these aids—she waved her arm in airy dismissal of the marvels of radiology—to help me to tell her what was wrong, that was my business and I should bear the charge myself.

If a patient came without a fee and said so, we were ready enough to excuse him, and certain emergency cases could be expected to have no money when they were brought in. One such woman was a Diviner who was led in, dumb, one morning to out-patients. 'I have brought this woman to you, doctor, in the condition in which all women should be,' said her attendant, adding hastily as my eye slipped to her waist in practised estimation of her condition, that she was unable to speak since the morning. Her jaw was dislocated and her mouth wedged painfully open.

It was easy to reduce. 'Thank you,' she said with relief as the jaw clicked into place.

'That will be one shilling,' I said, pleased with myself.

'I haven't got any money.'

'Why didn't you say so before?'

'Please, doctor, I couldn't speak when I came in.'

I saw the justice of that, but raised my hands in mock wrath. 'In that case I shall have to put it out again.'

She shrank for the threatened explosion, opened her mouth in dismay and dislocated her jaw again.

When I had reduced it again the second time, we bandaged the jaw firmly before the outbreak of any fresh argument, and I felt obliged to treat her without charge.

For In-patients there were official fees with a ceiling set at two pounds. By reason of a short stay, bills might be less, but they could not be more. Apart from maternity cases—where, we argued, a woman had all of nine months to think the position over and take steps to gather the fee as the weeks of her pregnancy advanced—we were not insistent upon rapid payment of these accounts which were given on a slip of paper at the time of discharge. Rogues never paid at all, the poor were not expected to pay, the well-to-do often omitted to pay, leaving about forty per cent who came back over a period of months or years and honourably discharged their debts.

It was widely believed that any money paid over went towards the doctor's already tremendous wealth. It did little good to deny that this was so, and except for countering overt bribery we seldom tried to correct the impression.

Patients whose disorders necessitated a long stay in hospital often wearied of their treatment, and sent the oldest and most pathetic-looking member of their family to beg their release for which, it was made clear, payment would be made above that sum which would appear on the bill.

'But your daughter isn't staying in hospital because she hasn't paid,' you explain, 'this is a disease for which she will need a long time to get well.'

'Doctor, I am alone at home and have no one to look after the cattle.'

'It's no use talking like that, mother; she is not ready to come home yet.'

From the folds of her garments she brings out a battered tin box, opening it to reveal an encouraging number of bank notes. 'Please, doctor?'

'I tell you, it's no good; she is still having treatment.'

Unbelievingly the old lady restores the tin box to its soiled, mysterious hiding place. Perhaps the notes were not sufficient? 'I'm asking nicely, doctor. We are old patients of yours and we don't want her to have to run away'—this with a pained expression at my unreasonableness, which contrasts so sharply with her willingness to please.

'Go away and forget about it,' you say in exasperation, and take up the work in hand with tremendous concentration until, disappointed in you, she walks away and down to the wards to confer again with her daughter.

CHAPTER FIVE

They're all the same

ALONG the Western border of the district runs the Buffalo River. It is a moody water, at times little more than an opalescent stream meandering in its own broad sandy bed; at other times, when there has been heavy rain at its sources in the Drakensberg range or when furious thunder storms have passed over the farm lands through which it flows, it comes down bank-high, its waters turned to liquid mud, smelling of decaying vegetation. Then, on its undulating surface ride whole tree trunks, bucking, nudging the piles of the bridges, turning and slipping past the farmsteads, plunging at last down the cataracts which race between the red cliffs a mile or two below Rorke's Drift.

Across the river are the European-owned farms of Natal; not the vast wealthy farms of the Transvaal or the Karoo country of the Cape, but modest holdings of about two thousand acres apiece. Along the river banks are flat, arable lands of good, alluvial soil, but the ground rises not far from the river so that the majority of the farm is steep and rocky, good for cattle but unsuitable for the plough. Long winter droughts and the low fertility of the earth preclude intensive cultivation and erosion has scored ugly marks over the lower hill slopes. It is good farming land but not the best, and the farmers, though well able to live on their holdings and maintain a comfortable standard of life, are not considered rich in a country of rich men.

Their homesteads are bungalows, home-designed and, as often as not, home-built, having a likeness to one another sufficiently marked to constitute an architectural style. The core of the house is the original pioneer home, built by the grim bewhiskered old man whose oval portrait, popeyed and hand-tinted, shares the wall above the fireplace with the mounted brows of buffaloes and a few stuffed buck's heads. Built in stone the old house may have had a couple of rooms and a lean-to kitchen; its windows small and deep-set, its low ceiling of stretched hessian.

Outward from the core, the house would grow by the enclosure of the surrounding verandah to make bedrooms for the patriarch's increasing family, leaving the inner rooms, which were never very bright, darker than ever. Here, propped in four-poster beds, grandmothers may still be found whose lives, like the light itself, are fading slowly to extinction.

However the house develops the verandah remains the distinguishing feature of the style and even when a new homestead replaces the old, is seldom omitted from the designs. It is the part of the house more used than any other save, perhaps, for the kitchen; it is the outdoor lounge, the meeting place of friends, the very best place for an evening glass of beer or a quiet, thoughtful smoke; it is the place to hang—out of the sun yet open to the breeze—the strips of drying meat which, for all their disgusting appearance, are both tasty and sustaining when chewed in the open air; on it the farmers wife tends her pot-plants, ferns and succulents in green painted tins or flamboyant garden urns of red earthenware; it is the place to hang a saddle or to rear a motherless lamb.

Round the back of the house is the kitchen, filled with an unexpectedly large number of servants. It is a place of activity from a full hour before sunrise until long after the evening meal has been served in the dining-room. Even later than that, if you enter in search of hot water for a bed-time cup of tea, you are likely to stumble over one or two wrapped figures of kitchen maids asleep on the floor. Here is carried out the greasy ritual of washing up; morning and evening the cream-separator whirrs and pings; there is bottling to do in the season of the wild peaches and the recurrent making of syrupy jams and sticky crystallized fruits. The cooking is done on a classical kitchen stove; a cast iron, black-leaded, upright stove in the grand manner, demanding a ceaseless sacrifice of timber, grumbling when the wind turns contrary and puffing soot in the faces of the sweating acolytes who tend it.

Apart from the youths who pull and draw the double handed saw in the yard, cutting the sacrificial timber, there are usually two maids dedicated to the service of the stove, buxom Zulu wenches whose full round bosoms and broad hips strain the seams of the discarded cotton dresses given them by a generous but small-boned mistress. A few smaller children, too young to be left at home, play on the floor near an old woman who, with flicks of a pointed kitchen knife, is stripping the hard bark of a pumpkin.

This overburden of servants which seems to be necessary to keep even the smallest household of Europeans at the unpretentious level of rural living, is not the result of any calculated domination, nor has it any sinister implications whatever. It is almost accidental, a living memory of the good old days when the English middle-class family had at least two maids, and the better-to-do a great many more. Servantless now, we are inclined to look for improper motives, taking to ourselves moral merit for doing our own washing up, glorying unduly in our aprons. On the farms servants are aplenty; life is geared to their continuing ministrations and the stove will remain the black mistress of the kitchen until there is no one left to stoke it and there are no brown arms to saw the firewood. Then, the farm kitchen will be re-equipped with labour-saving devices and women will bottle their own fruit over a fire of smokeless fuel.

The source of all these workers—men for the farm, women and girls for the kitchen and dairy, children to act as companion-nursemaids to the children of the house—is the homes of the squatters. Living on every farm are a number of African families, partly from choice, by arrangement with the farmer, and partly because they were born there and see no reason to change a mode of living which suits them well enough. They have a portion of the farm for their own use, an acre or two of arable, grazing for a certain number of beasts and a reasonably secure tenancy. In return they are obliged to render six months' service every year to the farmer, the other six months being theirs to work elsewhere for gain, to cultivate their own land or, if they so desire it, to sit philosophically and do nothing at all. Every member of the family may be called upon to take a turn in service, from the youngest daughter to the head of the home and in the case of children this may interfere with their schooling. Most farmers are willing to arrange the service so that it coincides with the school holidays and does not prejudice the children's chances of educational advancement. The service is nominally unpaid, but increasingly farmers are giving a small stipend to their male workers at least, partly from a stirring of conscience, partly as a means of perpetuating a system which should have died out long ago.

It is a form of labour which is open to the most flagrant abuses, yet though there have been instances of overt slavery on farms in the maize-growing area of the Transvaal, with the virtual imprisonment of labourers at the end of the day's work, there have been no scandals in our neighbourhood and the relationship between the farmers and their squatters has in general been satisfactory, and often one of notable affection and trust.

2

The farmers come to view their tenants much as a father looks upon a wilful, wayward child; as *their* boys and *their* girls; theirs to discipline, theirs to do good to, theirs to command through the long day. It is a brittle, unsure relationship into which the labourer, who has no incentive to do better, slips cheerfully enough, behaving as he is expected to do, more like a youth than a grown man. For so long as the master and the boy do not demand too much of each other all goes well. If friction does occur the labourer has no redress, since to withhold his labour is both illegal and likely to result in his eviction. By the same token the employer has no power, by incentive-pay or otherwise, to increase the efficiency of the squatter's work—which leaves him only his bare fists or a hide whip with which to step up production. But to beat the boys is becoming less respectable than it was and also more dangerous since the rights of legal redress have become more widely known among the workmen.

A lifetime of the squatter-farmer relationship leads, by its familiarity, to over-dependence on the one hand and an unhealthy sense of possession on the other. Most farmers show a kindly interest in the welfare of their labourers, bringing them to hospital when they are ill, transporting them in their own cars, paying for whatever attention is required. Naturally they want to know what is wrong and see nothing remarkable in asking the doctor outright for a full account of the disease, the treatment and the expected length of convalescence. It is universal practice; white children bring grown women round to the out-patients. 'I've brought our girl, doctor; mommy says will you please look at her and tell us what is the matter with her?' Traders write: 'Doctor, please be so good as to tell me what is wrong with my boy. I enclose half a crown.' To be offended by this rough good-will would be to assume an overweening righteousness in medical ethics, for there is no improper motive behind the questions, only real interest and a desire to help. But vigilance is necessary to counter this benevolent but nosey interest, and to avoid breaches of confidence without falling into priggishness requires more verbal skill than I possess.

Mrs van der Walt was a kindly and sensitive farmer's wife who took her duties to her servants seriously. She had more than a suspicion that her kitchen maid was pregnant and was well within her conventional rights when she brought her along for me to say whether or no her suspicions were well-founded. As it happened I knew the servant already, but I made a further examination which more than confirmed her mistress's guess.

'Mrs van der Walt wants to know if you are pregnant,' I said at the end. 'May I tell her that you are?'

'No, please, doctor, I don't want her to know.'

'She'll find out soon enough, won't she?'

'Not her,' Rosta shook her head. 'I'm going to run away next month, and she'll never know.'

I went outside to Mrs van der Walt. 'Well, doctor?'

I took fright before those slightly amused, lifted eyebrows and prevaricated : 'She's not too bad—nothing to worry about or anything like that.' Put that way it sounded a bit thin and I tried again : 'It is possible she may not be able to continue working for you for very much longer,' I added.

'But is she going to have a baby, doctor?' This was the direct question I had dreaded.

'I'm afraid I cannot tell you that,' I said stiffly. She took it the wrong way, and I could see her writing me off as an incompetent.

'Do you mean you don't *know*?' She rode the sentence up the scale of disbelief.

'I'm afraid I cannot tell you,' I repeated unhappily.

Mrs van der Walt loyally paid her fee and left, followed by the impenitent Rosta who carried her twenty-eight weeks equivocally.

In due season Rosta, who in the end had not run away, went out of the kitchen one morning and had her baby in a gully out of sight of the house. She wrapped the child in a piece of mutton-cloth and buried it lightly in the earth wall of the gully before starting back towards the house. Returning, she met Mrs van der Walt who had followed her, never having been wholly convinced that Rosta's appearance was solely the result of good feeding.

'What have you done with it, Rosta?' she asked sternly. Rosta, exhausted and afraid, burst into tears. Saying nothing she led her mistress to where the baby lay in its cocoon of cloth. Surprisingly, the little creature was lusty and bellowed all the way up to the hospital, although Rosta herself sat inert and bleary on the back seat. I admitted them to hospital under the battery of Mrs van der Walt's reproachful forgiveness. 'Why, *why* didn't you tell me, doctor?' she kept asking. 'I'd have helped her prepare for the baby and she could have had it in hospital safely.'

And I knew she would have done all that and much more for her girl, which would have been so much better than the visits of the police and the formal charge of attempted murder, even though the case was thrown out by the magistrate.

3

'And are they grateful for all you do for them?' twittered Mrs Vermeulen. Not that she really wanted to know, for the European woman brought up with the Natives knows that they are not, but indulging herself in the tea-time occupation of missionary-baiting. Margaret sighed—the gambit was already distressingly familiar—'They come when they are ill,' she said simply.

This spineless reply launched Mrs Vermeulen on a course of instruction through the narrows of which she sailed her stout barque, comfortably unaware of the jutty rocks of implication which lay so close under her hull. 'I'm always very good to my servants; good, but very strict,' she began, glancing round for support from the other ladies gathered in that lino-leumed drawing-room. 'They know that I mean what I say when I tell them to do something, and they're really very good; I don't know what I should do without them.' True, Mrs Vermeulen; you would have to wash up and cook, and darn Mr Vermeulen's socks and put your children to bed.

'*But*'—she underlined the word a couple of times as she wiped away a tiny speck of cream that had fallen on her blossomed bosom, 'I won't stand any nonsense from them. If a girl is cheeky I just say, "Out you go, my girl," I say and—and—' she waved a cream horn in her search for the right phrase—'out she goes!'

There was a little stir of approval at Mrs Vermeulen's firmness. 'One girl—that girl Hetty—*you* remember her, dear, don't you?' she checked references with her hostess and continued—'she was with me ever so long, practically looked after Dirkie since he was a baby—of course I couldn't feed him myself; the doctor said it would affect my heart if I did, and you know what I suffer from *that*—and was so good.' She took breath. 'Where was I? Oh, yes; she looked after my baby until he had got his two-year-old teeth and I gave her *everything,* all my morning dresses and you remember that white plastic handbag? Well, I gave her that, too. Well, one morning she didn't come with my tea—and I'm no good if I don't get tea in the morning—"Hetty! Hetty!" I called, "Hetty, come here!" But she was nowhere to be found, so I sent Isaac down to look for her. Her room was empty, she was gone!'

Since most of the ladies present must have undergone similar experiences, Margaret thought they put up a very polite rustle of interest indeed.

'She had gone, and taken everything. Her room was *filthy!* After all

59

I'd done for that girl she had just run away. Of course I learnt afterwards that she'd gone with the van Zyl's garden boy, but what I mean to say is, they're all the same.' There were nods of approval; they are all the same.

Hearts lifted in thanks, so often over so little; blessings of heaven for the motorist who stops and gives a lift; painful letters of thanks for a cup of tea when Tembinkosi died—and you put milk and sugar in it too; thanks for helping my husband to get a pension; thanks for opened blind eyes; thanks for my baby; thanks for letting me sit in your church. *Domine non sum dignus.*

CHAPTER SIX

A Web of Clinics

I

MR BIRKINSHAW, who managed the trading store at the Northern end of the district, sold postage stamps with a deep sense of vocation, seeing his postal agency as a service to the public; a service which he maintained meticulously for many years without a break and without expectation of even a long week-end. He was a keen follower of football, had grave doubts about the probity of clergymen, and wrote his accounts with the utmost neatness, using a steel pen. He was a generous benefactor of the hospital and of many other individuals besides. His store was typical of the dozen or so trading posts scattered through the district, buildings more or less dark in a dim, commercial way, festooned with old military great-coats, scarves, bicycle wheels, axes, boots and hanging fly-papers, with, around the walls, shelves reaching upward to the ceiling. These shelves in their turn housed an infinite variety of articles, curry powder, carriage bolts, bolts of coloured cloth, kettles, writing paper, flat irons and lolli-pops; bins in the centre of the floor were full of maize, flour, millet and sugar about which the flies moved in nervous, saccharine bliss.

The verandah, a corrugated iron lean-to supported on decaying wooden posts, was piled with fleeces and hides stiffened in the dry air into two dimensional farmyard animals. At the ploughing season there were bags of fertilizer and green single-furrow ploughs raising their handles in iron supplication.

Over this kingdom Mr Birkinshaw ruled with two African viziers behind the counters—one on groceries, sweets and paraffin, the other on blankets, soft-goods and hardware—and day by day served the community for fifteen years. He knew his customers, the men who passed up and down from the cities, the wives, the mothers, the girls, the sweet-begging herd boys, the bad and the good. He gave credit from kindness to those whom he knew could never pay; he gave credit to the wealthy and made a just return by doing so; and he got annoyed with his customers from time to time, but not more often than was reasonable. For the lonely and unpopular he had a lasting concern; perhaps his own solitary life made him particularly sensitive to the unhappiness of those beyond the pale of normal human companionship.

Which was the reason why he befriended James Brown.

What Brown's real name was I do not remember, but he had adopted the one by which he was universally known after long service as an African clerk with a commercial firm of that name. He used to sign it in violet ink over a flourish of Elizabethan proportions at the foot of the designs which he produced for Mr Birkinshaw's and my inspection. These designs, drawn on the back of cigarette boxes or display posters, were complicated representations of wheels, cogs and rollers with a brief description of their purpose—a loom or a carding machine—and a dedication to his most gracious Majesty King George V, from his Majesty's most humble and obedient servant, James Brown. He was normally content to show them to us and return again to design further, improved models. Less often, Mr Birkinshaw had to exercise tact to dissuade him from sending the designs direct to Buckingham Palace. He had an infectious if rather secretive smile and was devoted to Mr Birkinshaw, for whom he did odd jobs working at a feverish pace, the sweat pouring from his chin and staining the khaki shirt which was the latest present from his friend and benefactor. He lived in a small, round house with a maze of wires, batteries and dead bulbs in the roof. 'My private line,' he would smile when asked what they were for. 'They ring me up most evenings.'

2

Mr Birkinshaw was one of the first to give us facilities at his store for holding district clinics. A dispensary had been started there before we came, but for several reasons, of which the vile road out to the store was the chief, it had died by the time of our arrival and had to be restarted. It was conducted in a small room built on to his storage-shed and half at least of its floor space was taken up by bales of second-hand flour bags which Mr Birkinshaw sold to the older women for petticoats. Under the eaves of the main shed was draped a huge comb of wild bees. Normally an industrious, peaceful community, the bees resented our intrusion and within minutes of the clinic's being established for the day they came creeping down the walls from the ceiling and swarming up through the floorboards, filling the air with the hum of their excitement. They dashed themselves against the window panes and tangled themselves in our hair, stinging us painfully on the scalp. Some drowned in the wash-basin and more were boiled in the sterilizer, but we affected to ignore these floating bodies, just as we kept silence when they stung us.

The clinic at Mr Birkinshaw's became one of the most important in our plan for a district-wide service. With ten such dispensaries we made sure that a doctor reached within a reasonable walking distance of any home in the area at least once a fortnight. Seven miles was the radius that we accepted as a reasonable walking distance, a journey which does not look too bad on a map, but which must seem an intolerably long one to a patient with a fever or to those who march, step by sickening step, to the rhythm of the throbbing of an inflamed ear. To these clinics pregnant women walk the field paths with aching hips and grandmothers carry infants and young children on bent and scrawny backs. Girls saunter along, laughing, careless, boy-befriended, more for the fun of the thing than for much else, for clinic is a gala for the healthy quite as much as it is a relief to the cramped belly or the worried mind.

It is also the time for dressing up. Although there are always the poor and tattered, the standard of dress among many of the patients is remarkably high. Inexpensive Swiss petticoats in machine-embroidered nylon are almost a uniform for women who dress in western style, with—as a concession to missionary influence—sad bloomers of blue cotton underneath. The brassiere, a support introduced only recently into Africa, is usually, from the ungenerosity of its cut, less than fully suited to the robust Zulu figure.

Dresses, skirts and blouses are of great elegance and often in perfect taste, well matched with correct accessories, the handbags and the hats, and, chief of all, the charming Japanese umbrellas which can be bought cheaply at the stores. How this brilliance of dress is managed on the pitifully small incomes of many of our patients and, more remarkable still, how the washing and ironing are done so neatly in even the simplest homes, is an unfailing wonder.

With the healthy young men away in the towns, the relatively few men who attend the clinics are shabbily dressed in token of their poverty; but where they are fit enough to earn a wage, the same high standard—which puts me continually to shame—persists among them, too. There are, of course, the intermediate stages; flamboyant costumes made up of patched trousers, fancy shirts, phosphorescent ties, yellow dusters, bangles and beads, but it is generally true that the well turned out African is the best dressed man in South Africa; certainly he is in relation to his income.

But it is the babies of prosperous families who stand out. Everything about them—the woollen bootees, the damp, plastic pilch which encloses if it does not entirely suppress the natural humours; the tiny cotton vest with the coloured ribbon at the neck; the smocked nylon dress; the lantern-cowled bonnet—all is neat and spotless. A reactionary love for infant nakedness and a personal distaste for the stuffier-smelling baby powders, spoils my enjoyment of this splendour, but women who take this much trouble with their baby's clothes, also do well in other fields of child-rearing. Their sleek and lovely infants are an object lesson to the less fastidious mothers who sit beside them, grubbily awaiting their turn to be seen.

Hlubi's people, whose home extends as far north along the border of the district as Mr Birkinshaw's store, dress less after the white South African pattern and more in a modified traditional way of their own. The main garment is the petticoat, a gathered skirt of cotton print, which, as it ages, is covered by another skirt-petticoat of the same type of cloth. A bulky, peasant effect results when from ten to fifteen of these petticoats are superimposed. They swing gracefully and hang discreetly from the broad hips of the women. A simple bodice—one only—and a blanket around the shoulders completes the body covering, to which is added a flaming turban in turquoise or cerise cotton, pinned with a koh-i-noor diamond set in a rolled-gold mount.

3

Four mornings a week the clinic van sets out from the hospital with the driver, the nurse and the doctor in the cab, and behind, under a home-made canopy, ride patients returning after treatment. Beside them in the back are the fitted boxes containing all the equipment for the clinic; their own innumerable bundles, a fowl or two as presents, water in a drum for washing purposes and for filling the radiator when necessary, and as many extra people requesting lifts as can safely be fitted in. Even were he far less useful than he is at the clinic, the driver would still be included as a member of the team since the long slow journeys over the bumpy roads provide the time for reading professional journals and keeping reasonably up to date with recent developments in the medical world.

Nor is the driver's work over when he has negotiated the dusty winter roads or skidded through the silken mud of the summer wet season. At the clinic he marshals the patients, writes their names in the register, accepts their fees and gives out the medicines prescribed. In a cellophane-wrapped pharmaceutical age it is easy to scoff at the old galenical remedies, Mist.

Expect. Sed. for the coughs; Mist Alba. for ill-defined biliousness; Pot. Cit : et Hyoscyamus for the young ladies in the early weeks of pregnancy; Salicylates for rheumaticky old joints and all-pervading Cod Liver Oil which sets into toffee as it dries on the side of the bottle. But these ancient remedies have their very real uses and have stood the test of time; they are inexpensive, they do no harm, they relieve symptom and they retain the patient's interest until the next visit, when an estimation of progress may be made. In the conditions for which they are used—the coughs and colds and abdominal retributions for parties—there is in any case no specific treatment and, wrapped as they were in our fathers' day, in glazed white paper, and sealed with red wax by the deft fingers of the dispenser, they did all the good that could be done and have not lost their significance entirely even to-day.

About five out of every hundred cases examined at the clinics are ill in the sense of needing hospital treatment; the remainder suffer from mild ailments, require ablative dentistry or are in one or other stage of reproduction. Very few indeed are malingerers, fewer still are hunters after certificates; it is all pure medicine, with an enviable freedom from form-filling and the fear of litigation.

Yet bread is not earned, even in this arcadia, without sweat. Real difficulties arise from the patients' conception of a correct approach to the doctor. In Europe it is accepted as the patient's duty to put his doctor in possession of any relevant facts about his symptoms, their intensity and duration, the history of any previous attacks of the same nature, and any other information which the doctor may require to guide his examination and arrive at a diagnosis. Among African patients such communicativeness is considered to be mere weakness, giving away far too much and leaving no opportunity for the doctor to demonstrate his skill for which he is being paid. Such complaints as are made frequently owe more to a sense of the picturesque and a respect for tradition than to the literal Anglo-Saxon truth.

The principal symptom proffered by the women is 'bladder.' Men, pointing to the same area of the lower abdomen, complain of 'kidneys' —which are believed to lie in this unexpected site—or the 'strings of the groins,' which comprise a mystical region whose significance has so far eluded me.

Included in this bizarre symptomatology are disorders lying in the wide clinical pastures of abdominal surgery, gynæcology, psychosomatic disorder associated with childlessness and, rarely, actual disease of the bladder itself.

So far as they mean anything at all, the traditional words may be interpreted solely as 'I am drawing your attention to the lower part of my abdomen; it is for you to find out what is wrong.' A careful examination and a few questions artfully slipped into the conversation—direct questions are countered by evasion—will usually discover what is amiss, but at the close of a long clinic or after a sleepless night at the hospital, this repeated failure to recount the symptoms may irritate beyond endurance and lead to fraying of the temper. It is not wholly from a love of periphrasis that symptoms are hidden from the doctor; most patients are unfamiliar with analytical thinking and find it difficult to express themselves in anything like a logical manner.

Each patient, then, comes with his question; it is the doctor's first duty to formulate the question and then, so far as he is able, he must try to give the answer. Which means that there is an extra step in the consultation which must be taken if the interview is to prove successful. Tracing that step is laborious and repetitious :

'What is troubling you?'

'Bladder.'

'In what way is it troubling you?'

'It is painful.'

'Have you any children?'

'No.'

'How long have you been married?'

'A long time.'

'How long?'

'Seven years, this is the eighth year.'

'Do you want a baby?'

'Yes, doctor.'

'Then why not say so? Why do you complain of pain in your bladder when you really want a baby?'

'Because it is painful.'

The reference of symptom to an innocent organ is not, of course, confined to Zulu patients. The heart receives, in western society, blame for many twinges more properly the responsibility of the over-full stomach; our own word 'hysteria' stems from the Greek word for the uterus. Is it possible that well-to-do English ladies of the seventeenth century consulted their medical advisers in the same roundabout way which is to-day in vogue among the Zulus?

Interpretation, until the newcomer has enough Zulu to check its accuracy, can obscure still further what already lacks clarity. But interpretation is preferable to the misunderstandings that can arise from a hopeful nodding of the head and random yeas and nays in response to excited observations in a foreign tongue. I nearly admitted a horse to the wards by trying to pretend I understood a message which seemed to go something like: 'Would you come and see my father's leg which was injured by some barbed wire while he was riding his horse.' Because of distance, it is seldom possible for us to visit any home more than once, which makes us advise hospital treatment for all but the simplest disorders. 'I can only come if your father agrees to return to the hospital for stitching if necessary,' I said.

The messenger looked a little awkward. 'But, doctor . . .' he began.

'No "buts" about it,' I emphasized. 'If I go you must be willing to let him return with me if I say so.'

The out-patient nurse joined in at that moment, and so saved me from sinking further into the linguistic mud. 'I think, doctor,' she whispered in English, 'he means that it was the horse's leg that was cut by the wire.' I sent the astonished messenger away with a bottle of antiseptic, telling him carefully through an interpreter not to give the medicine to the horse to drink, but to apply it to the affected part.

Later, I like to think we made sufficient progress with the beautiful and expressive Zulu language to avoid making our friends blush for us, but I am not sure even about that, for there are only slight differences in the prefixes of words to mark the narrow distinction between the polite, useful form and the very rude. It is not likely that beginners should walk the verbal tightrope entirely without a slip.

4

The clinic premises are in the gift of the traders at whose stores they are held. In some places the provision is excellent, with a table, chairs and an examination couch. In other centres we work in garages or among decaying onions on a storeroom floor. Occasionally we share shelter with a solitary fowl who, broody and silent, is a witness to all that passes.

Under the conditions of most clinics it is difficult to ensure privacy. Even if the driver is able to keep the doorway clear of waiting patients there remains the need for speedy turnover. Attendance may be well in excess of one hundred patients, with the time limited by the hours of daylight and the need to return to cases awaiting attention at the hospital.

It is possible, though not desirable, to attend to three patients at a time, with one preparing for examination, one already on the couch, and the third dressing at the close of the interview.

Behind this haste lies the ever-present danger of missing an important symptom or failing to make an early diagnosis. The danger is all the greater for there being little expectation of the patient's return if his symptoms persist or the condition advances. Only too often, if the first attendance results in no immediate relief, the patient loses confidence and renounces the whole panoply of modern medicine—its knowledge, its skills and its integrity—in favour of magic and spellbinding; and all this because of the individual doctor's failure, in the rush of a clinic, to stretch his capacity to include just one more patient.

At first, attendance was pitifully small. We knew, or guessed, that every home harboured its sick person; yet, though we passed scores of homes on our way to and from each clinic, there would be only ten or fifteen people who came and of these, few or none at all would be really ill. Slowly the tide began to turn in our favour; with, at first, an increase rather in quantity than in quality, and the conditions that we were called upon to treat remained simple disorders which, while they afforded little stimulation to our medical curiosity, were at least capable of relief.

Only later, after we had examined and treated the minor ailments of the multitude for a year or two was there an improvement in the quality of the work we were asked to do. One by one, patients were brought to us who required more skilled management and who were, to our surprise, content to receive it at our hands. Tragically often we were presented with conditions too far advanced for any useful treatment at all. So many disorders which ultimately destroy us come at first in apparent benignity, wearing a falsely-smiling aspect which may at times deceive the elect and will certainly confuse the ignorant. Where there was pain, or where the serious nature of his illness was apparent to the patient, it was usually easy to persuade him to come to hospital, but in the early stages of their diseases, when treatment was likely to be most effective, many were unwilling to be admitted. There are always reasons why it is impossible to take time off to be ill, reasons shared equally between the business executive and the simplest peasant; deals to complete, the dead to bury, crops to hoe or reap. And when reasons fail, excuses are multiplied: 'I am alone at home,' announces a wife from a polygamous household. 'I am alone at home,' says her husband. This may be true in the literal sense and Mrs Njoko may have the sole and unrelieved care of four children while her man is away at the mines, but more often it is true only in a figurative way. 'I am the only Mrs Njoko, the only one of me, left at home and who will look after my children, my cattle and my fields when I am in hospital?'

'But what about your husband's mother?'

'Yes, yes, she is at home, too, but I don't think she would help me.'

It is a recurrent problem, and in a society without home helps and lady almoners it is probable that there is real hardship in many cases. Yet, if the inclination to come for treatment is there, the homes of most people are found to be rich in relations only too willing to assist.

Knowing from hard experience that it was unusual for patients who promised to come 'next clinic' to appear at all, we had to plan treatment on the assumption that we might never see an individual patient again. This was neither difficult nor important in the trivial disorders for which most people consulted us; but what was the right course of action when faced with an early cancer? It would be indefensible to offer anything which might lull the patient into false security where no bottle of medicine or magical injection—and many patients demanded both—could do any good whatever. Only one possible route was open; to offer hospital care, with surgery and radiotherapy where necessary, and then to stand by your decision. At the thought of surgery many would find themselves alone at home who might for a physician have managed to procure a home-minder, but it was no good hiding your intentions. True, it was not necessary to say bluntly that you were going to cut or skin the patient—as the Zulu phrase went—but to a direct question it was necessary to give a straight answer.

If the remedy that we prescribed was refused there was seldom any purpose in giving way to the patient's plea for that of his own choice, but it was a different matter when faced with advanced cases of disease beyond predictable recovery; then to be kind and to relieve pain is objective enough and we did our best for the patient in his own home.

Our refusal to compromise over curable illness was not popular, but there were unexpected people who saw the justice behind this unbending front. We gained the not very enviable reputation for being the doctors who always wanted to put you into hospital, and many passed our doors in search of less demanding medical advisers. One woman who had lost several previous children and had only one ewe lamb left to her, took the bus outside the hospital to see a doctor in the neighbouring town. There the child was given the injection that she desired and she and the baby returned home. But its condition continued to deteriorate and a few days later she came up, the moribund child in her arms, willing enough at the last for hospital treatment. Almost by a miracle the infant survived.

'Your baby was born here,' Margaret pointed out. 'Whatever prevented you from coming when she was ill?'

'I knew you'd take her into hospital,' was the reply.

5

Clinic has remained the great point of contact between the hospital and the people it serves; it is the sorting house where surgical sheep are divided from medical goats and both from the great body of complainants whose symptoms outweigh any evidence in them of organic disease. Here the patient is seen against his home background, we get to know his wife and his mother, the poverty or wealth of his home, the standards of food and hygiene by which he lives. It is the place, too, where we are made most aware of custom, that body of remembered lore which stabilizes society before the growth of individualism and the spread of literacy make written rules and policemen necessary to achieve the same object.

The guardians of custom are the elders and, where tribal ways still obtain, theirs is a force which cannot be ignored. It is the old ladies who take the new-born babies, recently discharged from the maternity ward at the hospital and see that their bowel is properly scoured from evil influence by the use of medicinal herbs and ritual enemas; it is the mothers-in-law who remove breast-fed babies from one or both of their daughter's breasts because the milk is 'bad for the child'; it is the fathers who decree a child's premature discharge from hospital to be present at a feast for the propitiation of a cross ancestor-spirit. And, although custom frequently works against what seems to be the best interests of the people themselves, steps towards change must be taken slowly and then only after the most careful reflection. The cohesive authority of the elders is enshrined in obedience to custom and where authority declines, and the respect that goes with it, there is only too often an alarming decay in family and community life. If, acting from the best motives, the reformer too hastily challenges the ancient sanctions, he may loose anarchy and lawlessness far worse than the evils he wished to remedy.

From our medical point of view, the rules governing the drinking of milk were particularly important. Milk, coming from cows which themselves are of more than merely economic importance to the Zulu family, is subject to strict prohibitions and well-defined rules which govern its use. It is a symbol of the blood-relationships within the family, for milk is only drunk within the clan and is not shared with strangers nor asked for by travellers. It is for this reason that the young wife is not permitted to drink milk when she comes first into her husband's home. She is new, untried and foreign; until she is established as a wife and as a daughter to the elders, she remains a stranger in the house. The prohibition lasts for at least a year, and sometimes longer, implying in the majority of instances that she will go through her first pregnancy without any milk at all in her diet.

In practice, this deprivation causes less trouble than might be expected, but the doctor may feel that he should try to get these young women to take milk at least during the latter months. A direct verbal assault, urging the bride herself to drink milk, produces more polite agreements than actual alterations in feeding habits. The way to the milk-pail is through the mother-in-law who, as keeper of the tradition, has also power to waive the prohibition under special circumstances and to grant the necessary permission. More mothers than might be expected prove co-operative, giving assent 'if you say so, doctor,' and it is always worth a try.

Like all the best principles, milk taboos can and should be broken when humanity, good manners and sound reasons demand the breach.

CHAPTER SEVEN

Boy with a Flute

I

THERE is too much of the morbid about hospitals, too much scrubbing and whispering, for any one to feel really at ease within their walls. When ill we are thankful for their services; the destitute and the aged are grateful for their shelter, but we are always glad when we are discharged and prefer to remember our stay in hospital in retrospect, even as we remember our schooldays, with gratitude, but also with relief at their passing.

Knowing that the tests, the innumerable blood samples, the whirling floor polishers and the clanking of dawn bedpans are all for our good, we grumble only to ourselves and our closest visitors. Good manners and a wholesome fear of our physicians and surgeons keep us from asking too often the question we should all like to put: 'When, oh when, am I going home?' It may have been the uninhibited nature of Mrs Dhladhla or the after effects of a long, debilitating illness that made her so importunate in her requests to go home. She had lain a week or so in the deaf, dark, muttering world of typhoid fever, and the aching dream had lifted only slowly. One day she sat bolt upright in bed and asked to be discharged. At that stage she was weak enough to soothe into silence.

'Not just yet, Mrs Dhladhla; wait until you are a bit stronger; just a few more days.'

But protein-rich foods filled out her frame and reinforced her determination. 'I must go home now,' she demanded.

Her evening temperature was still a degree or so above normal, and there was an ever-present danger of relapse. Soothing was replaced by military orders, and she lay a day or two more resentfully in bed, in part a prisoner of our firmness, in part defeated by a still frail body. I used to avoid those bright black eyes that were fixed on me whenever I went into the ward; their question was too insistent and I felt mean at my refusal to let her go.

One morning her animosity had melted away. She answered our 'good mornings' with a frankness that put us on our guard.

'My brother came yesterday,' she said,

'Oh, yes; how did he think you were looking?'

'He didn't say anything about that. He told me about my children.'

There was no mistaking the smugness behind her words. 'He said they were all lying sick at home.' The tears started to brim at her eyelids' edge; she sniffed, long and effectively. 'Sick, and all alone.'

This was a real poser, cleverly introduced. Past experience told my corrupted mind that the whole story had probably been invented for my express confusion, but on the other hand I could not be absolutely certain that these wretched children, the oldest of whom was ten, were not dying of fever unattended in a grass hut. I decided to call her bluff.

'I'll go and see them for you, if you like,' I said, 'then, if they are really in trouble I can bring them to you here.'

Mrs Dhladhla countered by calling my bluff in her turn. 'If you like, doctor, only it's rather a long way.'

'Oh? Where is it?'

'Esingabantu'—she mentioned a place forty miles away and seven miles from the nearest car-track.

'What is the best way to get there?' I was committed to appearing undismayed.

'You go through Qudeni and turn right.'

'Through Sutton's property, do you mean?'

'Yes, it lies below the store of Satan'—she used the Zulu corruption of the trader's name which he shared impartially with the Devil.

I tried to look cheerful as if I liked spending the whole night up—for that is what the journey would mean—bringing healing with me. But there was no alternative except to go and find out. 'But,' I added, failing a little, 'your story had better be true.'

She looked at me dead in the eye. 'Of course it is as I say,' she said with dignity.

'Of course,' I replied, remembering my manners.

2

That was how Margaret and I found ourselves driving out in the evening in a truck headed for the Qudeni mountain which by three o'clock that afternoon had already hidden its whale's back in chill mist. The growing moon was a day or two short of fullness but was still bright enough to take over some of the sun's work at dusk, a willing but not very effectual junior partner. Cold slips of mist broke off the mountain's cloud cover, shadowing the deep valley which we were skirting. Then the road rose into the cloud and our vision became a funnel of yellow headlights, blinkered by dark rows of tall, imagined pine trees standing in the blackness beyond the edge of sight.

A finger-post pointed the turn to the right which was barred by strands of barbed wire stretched across the road in the form of a gate. Margaret unhitched the loop of wire which bound this gate to its post; shapeless without tension it writhed on the ground before she pulled it out of the way. We bounced down the rutted lane, the grass between the tracks brushing the under surface of the truck and once a brace of partridge flew up from the long grass as we passed. Past the third gate we came upon a barn-like building of stone; here I stopped the engine and got out; everything was cold and blurred in the swirling mist which passed the headlamps with the preoccupied haste of a rush hour crowd through a station barrier. I moved through the flying vapour and, knocking on a side door of the fortress, roused a tattered servant. 'Whose house is this?' I asked.

'Satan's,' came the reply, and in that detached atmosphere I felt almost relieved when he added, shutting the door in my face, that Satan was not at home.

We left the car and went down the path used by the customers and their donkeys on their way to and from the store. It was a staircase of rock, hewn a little too large for human strides and our descent was a painful and jolting one. At a few hundred feet below the store the mist began to thin and the light improved enough to enable us to see a little ahead, but even before we emerged into the clear moonlight we heard footsteps, light, springing, accurate paces following us from behind. There was reedy music, too; three notes in a sweet repetition of sound, music older than melody, the ancient cadence of the trees, of small waters, of the eternal, careless, loving earth.

I suppose by daylight he would have been only a Zulu youth blowing bugle-wise on the pair of bicycle handle bars he was carrying; but it was not daylight. We were half a mile from the Devil's headquarters, bewitched by mist, and this young man, who so courteously offered to take us to the home we were seeking, might have been a leprechaun or, for that matter, an angel sent to guide us. It seemed fitting that someone should appear out of the darkness and greet us as if we were expected guests. Probably we told him whose home we were making for, but I am not entirely sure that he did not know already. He spoke not a word but went lightly on ahead, unerring into the moonlight. Our well-fed bodies

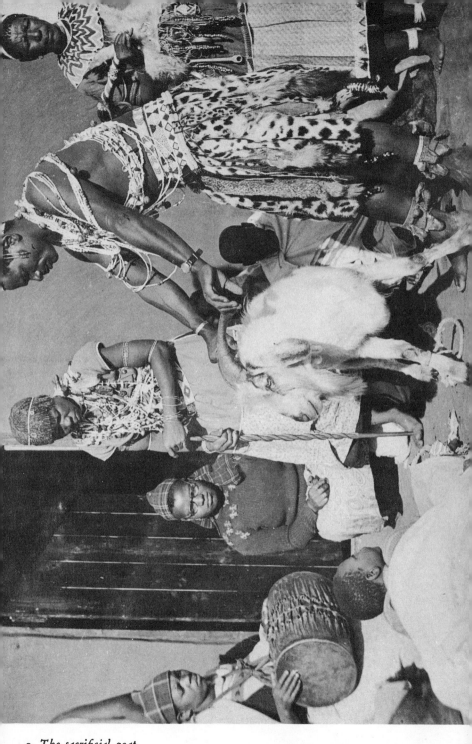

9. *The sacrificial goat*

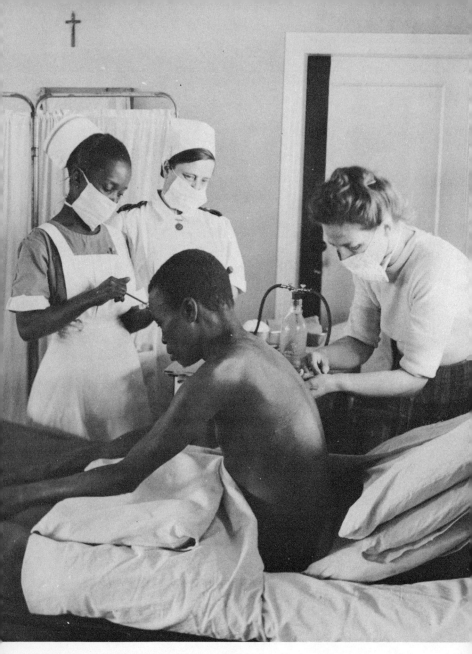

10. *Margaret Barker with patient*

followed his lean, undernourished frame in breathless pursuit; he skipped, we floundered between the rocks; he had breath to spare for piping, while our own lungs whistled and puffed with the exertion of keeping his flying figure in sight.

We came out from under the mist into the full radiance of the moon. In the fields beside the path the dried bones of the maize stems rattled as we passed, stirred by the wind; from time to time there were small mouse-scurryings within the grass, followed by a silence profound enough for the ear to catch the fearful, rushing beats of thumbnail hearts. Presently the youth stood still long enough to allow us to catch him up. 'This is the home,' he said.

We stood on the edge of what seemed a large collection of huts, hump-backed, silvered by the moon. A dog growled, burst into a frenzied baying and as suddenly stopped. There was no human sound at all from the clumped huts. Passing the stone wall of the cattle enclosure we could hear the sounds of deep, rhythmic breathing, the post-prandial sighing of near-apoplectic aldermen; we went in amongst the huts.

'I am knocking.' We announced ourselves traditionally.

'I am knocking, knocking,' we called again, but the thatch mopped up our voices.

From inside a hut to our left came a muffled grunt. Encouraged, we repeated our greeting.

'Who is knocking?'—the grunt took human tones.

'It is I, Barker, from the hospital.'

From within came sounds of disbelief and the scraping of a match on a box. Round the low door-frame we could see a faint light. Then a chain was withdrawn and the door removed from its frame; we could see in the smoky lamplit interior the blanketed forms of sleeping children. The man who had spoken to us crept out, head first, and stood up outside the hut. He was wearing a heavy overcoat in which he must have been sleeping.

'We come from the hospital,' we explained, but he did not reply. 'Lephina Dhladhla said her children were sick,' I added.

Again there was no response and for a few moments I thought I should have to carry on this conversation entirely by myself; then he bent down and put his head back through the doorway. 'Lena,' he called.

A second figure differentiated itself from the wrapped forms on the floor and a woman, also fully clothed, came out.

'Are the children ill?' he asked the woman.

'No.' The answer was ungarnished, but carried no hint of rudeness.

'The children are not sick'—he turned to me.

'Mrs Dhladhla said they were all sick and alone at home,' I insisted. He did not argue. 'Go in and look; they're all in there.'

Once inside we stood up, our eyes smarting from the sharp smoke of the dung fire in the centre of the floor.

'Sit down, sir. The smoke is not so strong down here,' Lena advised us and we humbly sat on the floor, where breathing was easier. The children were paraded for our inspection and, having come this far to see them, we examined each thoroughly and confirmed that they were all perfectly well. In the darkness outside again Dhladhla asked politely after his wife and when he might expect her home again, and then retired into the hut, plugging the exit with the wooden door and leaving us firmly on the outside.

The youth was still there. 'Come,' he said.

So he led us back along the paths by which we had come, as certain of his way as he had been while bringing us out, although the clouds had multiplied and the falling moon was hidden. At the bottom of the last hill he stopped.

'The path will take you safely to the top now,' he said, and began to move away.

'Hey! Wait a minute!' I said, feeling in my pocket for a tip.

All I had was 3s. 7d. in small change and I gave it to him. He took it politely, as Zulus always receive, with both hands outstretched, said a brief word of thanks and danced away into the darkness. We could hear his piping far down the valley as we climbed.

I am still unsure whether we thanked him rightly; 3s. 7d. was probably too little for a leprechaun and almost certainly too much for an angel.

CHAPTER EIGHT

Of Bricks and Water

THE gains of the early months, though slender in comparison with the huge problems of the district's health, were none-the-less sufficiently real to tempt us into expansion. Our influence extended little further than the destitute, but there were still enough of these to fill our few beds and overflow to mattresses on the floor. Bed space was reserved for the critically ill; with convalescence came descent, often to a space under the same bedstead in which a man had spent the fevered days and sleepless nights of his illness.

New buildings were going to be needed, but before they could be begun the land had to be cleared. Because the whole plot was only a couple of acres in extent and because what had to be hewn down and rooted out was not exotic vegetation but only a wilderness of gum trees and thigh-deep weeds, it does not follow that this clearance was a light task. Blue gum trees live for about eighty years and then die. They are tall and beautiful with multicoloured bark and drooping branches bearing narrow, scented leaves. Their very height attracts the lightning out of the boiling thunder-heads of summer afternoons and many of them are killed by the tearing bolts which split their soft trunks from top to bottom. But their vigour and fertility endeared them to the early missionaries who wanted shelter from the gales and dust storms of the spring and who felt at all seasons the nakedness of the grasslands after the leafy decencies of their home countries. The missionaries planted the avenues and the trees themselves planted the saplings that sprang up about their roots. Together with Port Jackson Willow, a low and pestilential bush, the young trees formed a scrub which soon extended to take up far too much mission land.

Whether lightning put a sudden end to their abundant growth, or whether the trees died at the close of their life span, the tall trunks remained standing—their lifeless bark hanging from them, sad as Twelfth Night decorations—as blanched monuments to a past enthusiasm for planting until someone had the energy and the means to cut them down. The hospital was bordered by more than a hundred of these trees, at sixty feet high still in the full flush of their growth. They drew from the land all that the land had to offer, giving their abundant seed in return until our small heritage was covered with hundreds of lusty saplings. Since we could grow nothing at all under the trees, not even a creeping grass to reduce the dust in the dry season and erosion in the rains, we set about felling them. At the same time we rooted up the scrub and chopped out a few gnarled crab-apple trees which grew in an untidy Linden Lea at the bottom of the garden.

The work of felling the major trees was given to Douglas Magwaza, at that time a young man in charge of the vegetable patch. He was not unsuccessful with his peas and vegetable marrows, but his real talent was for building; in later years he has developed into an excellent bricklayer and plasterer, but in the early days we were unaware of his gifts. He had to get rid of all but one or two out of the line of trees that ran along the northern border of the property, close to the hospital chapel of S. Anne and its round, thatched vestry.

Day by day Magwaza's men worked, digging, chopping at roots, climbing, roping the great branches, with the excitement gathering as the moment neared when each tree, its roots severed, trembled in balance and then, slowly at first and with gathering speed, fell rending and squealing to the earth. The team developed a surprising accuracy in landing the trees safely on neutral ground and all would have been well with the one that stood closest to the vestry had not an unexpected storm come up, quick and black, from the west. The men had gone to their dinner, leaving the roots exposed and partly divided when the storm struck. I was passing from the out-patients at the moment when the herald wind first moved the leaves; I watched the slender twigs bend and lift as the wind rose and saw first the branches and then the huge bole lean before the gust. At the instant when I realized that the tree could never recover from that obeisance but must fall, I remembered that the vestry-hut was temporarily occupied by three night nurses, sleeping there for silence' sake. For two attenuated seconds I watched the arc of its falling bring the trunk down on the little building, cutting off a third part of its circumference as a wire divides a cheese.

I do not know what my sick stomach expected my eyes to see as I ran towards the ruined hut, but the emergence through a window on the hut's undamaged side of broad hips, covered but not wholly disguised by a locknit nightdress, calmed my fears. One at least of the nurses had survived, and she the largest.

'Are you all alive?' I shouted to the now completely emerged nurse.

'Yes, we're all right,' she called back, 'but I'm afraid the hut is broken.' This was only too evident, but for the hut we had very little concern once we had all three nurses safely shivering outside.

For the actual building, once the land was prepared, we had a grant of £3,000 from the mission, which seemed to our inexperience a princely sum; enough certainly to build wards for all the patients that we might ever expect to have to treat. Six years as medical students and junior residents had given us no insight into the fundamentals of hospital design. We imagined in our ignorance that the wards *were* the hospital; we gave no thought at all to the chaste confines of the nurses' home and the sweating inferno of the boiler house. As for the laundry, that was represented in my mind as being almost magically disposed of at the moment when the neatly labelled bundles of linen had been stuffed down a shute in the wall and disappeared from our exalted medical vision. Of sewage disposal we knew nothing that was not immediately obvious at the depression of a lever or the pull of a chain. And water, that most precious commodity, came, of course out of taps.

2

Of all these things, and many more, we were to learn later by most painful teaching and bitter experience, but in those early days it was pleasing to spend our donor's gifts where the donors would wish them spent, on the provision of ward accommodation. There are to be found not a few men and women who will answer the call to help build wards, but most rare are those benefactors who ask no questions and require no memorial but a set of anonymous, infinitely prized W.C.s.

The building we planned was long, straight and ungarnished. Apart from a front and back verandah, there was no feature to disturb the rigid symmetry of it, and the materials from which it was built, cement blocks and corrugated iron, underlined the starkness of its conception. With a biannual coat of paint the building has come in time to have a rough distinction of its own, though no one would claim merit for it as an architectural achievement. Indeed, with so much of dreaming and so little of practical knowledge in its design, it has always seemed to me a wonder that this first essay in building has so well stood the test of time.

There was to be accommodation for thirty-two patients in two main wards, each with its own side-wards for the very ill or for occasional private patients. We often wandered through its half-completed shell, while the windows were still unglazed and the doorways gaping holes in the walls, wondering if we should ever have enough patients to fill its vastness; that it would not be big enough, was unthinkable. We fretted at the slow progress of the plastering and the delays in putting in the ceilings, and worried over the builders' wages and where we might get a plumber. The not over-difficult task of filling our cup of anxiety was left to the bishop who announced, when the building was about half completed, that he had given away £500 of our total grant to another hospital in even greater need than our own.

Yet, while the floors were still the natural earth, bearing a last crop of weeds before the concrete sterilized them for ever, patients began to overflow from the old buildings and take up a draughty, nomadic life on mackintoshes spread for them in the half-finished building. As the floors went in, the patients moved on, driven from their temporary resting place by the advancing concrete. A little later and they were permitted by a tolerant builder to return to their own damp, if weed free, piece of ground. In Crimean gloom, relieved at night only by the light of a hurricane lamp, they lay there, victims of who knows what night fears, and never once complained. This has always been the pattern; the unmurmuring acceptance of what could not be immediately altered. Their faith that discomfort was not for ever, nor by design, but a temporary condition to be remedied when possible, gave them a cheerful tolerance which earned for them an admiration we have never ceased to feel.

Then, when the completion of the building seemed to have put an end to our difficulties, came the first whisper that all might not be well with the water supplies. The windmill which toiled industriously through the windy nights of spring and idled away the light-aired summer afternoons, was not sufficiently under our control to be sure of maintaining a supply for the growing number of staff and patients. To bring the bore-hole under control, so that we could pump when we wished to and rest the well when our tanks were full, we ordered a motor-driven head to replace the windmill; an industrious ant to supplant the gay grasshopper.

It was a morning's work to dismantle the windmill and set up the new motor, which was turning over cheerfully by the time the dinner-bell rang. Up in the storage tanks water was entering at the full bore of the pipes. We went into lunch.

After coffee the engineer went down just to see that all was working satisfactorily. The engine was running faster than when we had left, and above its popping could be heard an unpleasant noise. It was a windy, ill-bred sound, like a schoolboy sucking the last drops from a lemonade bottle with a damp straw. Only this time the straw was a two-inch pipe, and the fluid, water. In a single lunch-hour the bore-hole had been pumped dry.

We stopped the little green machine that had so quickly exposed our weakness. If it were true that our well could not stand even an hour of efficient pumping, we were indeed in trouble. Without water all our plans might as well be thrown away; without water there could be no hospital at all. The engineer said his farewells—it was not his fault, but he seemed relieved to be going—leaving us standing in dismay, trying to escape the implications of our discovery. Perhaps it had been an unusually dry season? Were the leather washers worn on the valves? Could our water have been captured by the new bore-hole that the hotel had sunk a month or two ago? We wriggled and we floundered; we put on ten extra feet of piping at the bottom of the well; we made confident predictions of better days to come; but we were hooked by the one unavoidable truth—there was no water supply to the hospital even remotely capable of supporting the growing demands of the laundry, the kitchen, the wards and the garden.

A second bore-hole was sunk, deeper than any in the village, and that helped for a while, but by the next year, with the numbers of patients and staff swollen to twice their former size, this was wholly inadequate and we spent hours each day with not a drop of water in the tanks. The laundry women, finishing only such linen as there was water to wash, went home at noon; the cooks ran off water into pans whenever they got the opportunity; most of us went unbathed, if not unwashed for weeks together, and the water-closets, those symbols of progress, had to be closed and the earth privies reopened, their superstructures monuments each one of doomed hopes. Strangers, coming afresh into the situation were rightly horrified, but for us the drought had developed insidiously, with each day a pint or two less water than the day before, so that we had become resigned if not actually accustomed to hoarding the few gallons we could obtain each day.

Whenever it rained, the full misery of the crisis was relieved for a while, with every vessel in the hospital doing duty as a reservoir. Under these circumstances we could even manage a bath, but the storms were capricious and these small stores of water quickly used up. The cleaning women stuck it out, doing their best; the cooks muttered, but somehow produced the meals; the sisters stood by, sometimes complaining with their lips but resolute in their spirit; for myself I dared not contemplate the future.

Relief came at last through the Native Commissioner, but even then in a round-about way which none of us quite foresaw. It was he who arranged financial help from the Provincial Government, and he who charmed a neighbouring farmer into granting permission for us to take water from a stream on the hill above the hospital. And it was he who forgot to secure the water in a proper, legal manner.

The Native Commissioner was a direct man, enthusiastic to the point of being impetuous, forceful in the advocacy of his own viewpoint and not inclined to deal over tenderly with those who disagreed with him. The law's delays interested him not at all; verbal permission to tap the stream having been given, he started us on the pipe line which was to skirt the hill for three miles to the source of the water. No better testimony could be given to his strong personality—and to the affection in which he was held by those of us who knew him—than his persuasion of a Government department to pay more than £2,000 towards a water supply that was not secured by legal bonds. As for myself, who was I to doubt the issue? I was caught up in the fervour of the hour and set the labourers to work on the rocky country through which the pipe line was to run. They went at the job in the same hopeful spirit, embedding and blasting out, cracking the stiff rocks with fire and water, levering, shovelling, chiselling their way along the hill-side. We worked, all of us, with light hearts; at the end of the pipe line lay peace of mind and a bath every evening of our lives.

So that, when a small blue handwritten note came from a relation of the farmer's, saying that they had decided in family council not to allow us any water after all, the world broke up to the 'told-you-so's' of the spectators. It was no use arguing; we were dependent on good will and that good will had failed when all but the last few hundred yards of piping were laid. I went to see the Native Commissioner in his office. He sat without saying a word when I entered. Then, suddenly, he pulled a face—'Well, doc?'

I started to laugh and, in the bitterness of the moment, so did he.

'We've had it, sir.'

'Yes, we've had it.'

I felt very close to him just then; not because I was unaware that he had messed the whole thing up, which he had; but because I knew that, had I been making the arrangements myself, I should have made just as big an error.

Dhlame and his team of workers pulled the pipes up again with an enthusiasm almost equal to that with which they had buried them, while the Commissioner secured for us the legal rights over a soil conservation dam a mile away from the hospital in the opposite direction. Somehow or other he not only soothed the sore pride of the Treasury, but even brought the Provincial Water Engineer in person to plan our new supply.

The conservation dam stored about two million gallons of water of the colour and consistency of soup. Turning this stable clay-suspension into usable water gave the experts more trouble than they anticipated and ourselves even more than it gave the experts. On paper it is easy to precipitate a colloid by causing clumping of the minute particles until the aggregate is big enough to fall through the suspending water. So, at least, we were told; so my half-remembered schoolboy chemistry reassured me. And it was true, but not the whole truth. A third factor comes into real-life chemistry—the time taken for all this to happen. In theory, the floccules of clay were to be filtered off in a large steel cylinder provided by the engineering firm in charge of the installation. In fact, the water held on to its clay particles just long enough to pass through the filter before they were precipitated in the pipes beyond. The resultant thin, syrupy mud clogged everything with which it came in contact, settling in the boilers and silting up the storage tanks. There was plenty of water, but it could not flow from the taps. The situation remained unchanged.

We were forced to dismantle the pump-house wall to send back the filter to the engineering firm. They were cross, but they were also in the wrong, and had to receive, as gracefully as they could, their own again. We built a settling tank where, each night, the next day's water could be cleared of its contaminating mud, leaving us a ration of clear water to pump up to the tanks. We had water at last; not over abundantly, but in adequate quantities. Tension relaxed, the clouds lifted, and hope crept back into our councils; from the unfamiliarity of her face we realized she had been absent for longer than we had thought.

3

On the morning that the Administrator of Natal and the Executive Council were to visit the hospital, the main sewer became choked and very nearly spoilt the occasion. His visit was a formal affair and a great honour to our struggling hospital and, although he did not actually open our children's ward, his coming so nearly coincided with its completion that the two events are closely associated in my mind.

The children's unit, designed for rather more than forty children, was built as a series of small wards around a central, enclosed courtyard. The intention was to reduce cross infection in the event of an outbreak of infectious disease in any one ward, and in this it has proved largely successful. But there are other features of its design which are less satisfactory, in particular the difficulty of drainage from its having been built without an adequate footing to the walls. Storm water from the courtyard could only be run away into the main sewer, from which it was isolated by a trap, ensuring in the ordinary course of events that the decencies were maintained.

One hour before the Administrator's arrival a maize cob stuck in the sewer and acted as the nucleus for a complete stoppage. Behind the obstruction the water-level rose, the flow was reversed in the trap, and a stinking tide began to spread over the courtyard.

I was putting on a clean shirt when they came, panting, to tell me what had happened. 'Get Santo quickly,' I said.

Santo had replaced Jabajaba Zulu as sanitary man. 'He's there already, doctor.'

'Can't he unblock the thing?'

'He says he's tried, but he can't get the water to run away.' I stripped off my shirt. 'All right, I'll come.' I started to run down to the hospital.

Santo, whose origins were as obscure as the dialect he spoke, was feverishly passing lengths of wire down the pipe from a flooded manhole, making, with each thrust of his arm, unfounded accusations against the people whom he supposed had caused the stoppage. His head bobbed us as I approached. 'It's blocked up,' he said unnecessarily, 'and,' he bent again to the task, 'if I catch the . . .' but the rest was inaudible as the relentless rodding of the pipe went on.

'Here, Santo, let me have a go.' Arm deep in filthy water I thrust·at the blockage, wondering what I was going to smell like even if we could clear the thing in the next forty-five minutes. I worked away, with Santo muttering above me in the clean, spring air beyond the manhole.

'It's no good, Santo.' I gave up after five minutes of fruitless, disgusting toil. 'Let's try and clear upwards from below the block.'

We trailed jangling coils of heavy wire down the drive and opened the next manhole. It was empty. Between us we coaxed the wire up the pipe until we came to the place where our progress ended. 'Now!' I shouted, and we began to beat at the obstruction. Presently there was a snoring gurgle and a noise like a tube train approaching a station; I put out my arm. 'Quick, Santo, get me out of this.' Santo heaved and my feet just cleared the swift, evil flood as it roared down the pipe. Twenty minutes to go; twenty minutes to clean up; I could hear the women swilling buckets of clean water over the yard as I ran for my room, and I knew it would be all right.

4

In later years, when the children's ward was already classed among our older buildings, we were given a play-centre for convalescent children. This was paid for by a grant from the Africa Bureau in London and built by the voluntary labour of an interracial work camp. In its building the play-centre symbolized the possibility, however remote that may seem in present-day South Africa, of co-operation and friendship across the customary divisions of colour. Each member of that team put everything he had into the centre's construction; African members used their traditional skill in stonework; a European architectural student drew the designs and those who had no especial skills laboured through the hot summer days. In the evenings they would gather for discussions after their frugal suppers. They invited us to their undecorated table where we ate boiled potatoes from enamel plates, spearing their glassy substance with the uneven prongs of institutional forks. To these young men who worked through their summer holiday in order that our children might have the joy of a place of their own, came a reward paid in the coin of human understanding which I envied with all my heart.

Finished, the centre was an enchanting compromise between our hospital buildings and one of the shinier secondary modern schools which have so greatly cheered education's soiled face in Britain.

In the beginning, children from five years old were sent to play there for four hours each morning, learning by painting, modelling and carving. But the happy five-year-olds taught the fours, who passed the message on to the threes, that it was a denial of human rights to bar them from going, too. The protest that resulted was of sufficient intensity and duration to make us alter the rules. Thenceforth we included any child who, by reason of age or precocious advancement along the paths of childhood, could reach the building unaided. I sometimes see two-year-olds stumping along the path. 'Where are you off to?' I ask them. 'To school,' they pipe with a charming disregard for the niceties of terminology.

Mrs Nsibande is in control of the play-centre. A retired schoolteacher, she lives nearby in the police lines, where her husband is a constable. Under her eye the children paint, draw, model, carve and sew appliqué pictures with scraps of cloth. She is marvellously patient with the children and somehow brings out their latent talent. There is no lack of stimulus; through the large glass windows which fill the north-east wall of the building, the pupils observe with the gimlet eyes of children and paint what they see of their superiors with dreadful accuracy. What they do not see, their imaginations supply. There is retained, for all this keen observation, a strict sense of the orders of society. No egalitarian taint can be observed in the paintings, and where the hierarchy is represented, as it frequently is in ward scenes and groups of nurses, the great figure, painted an unflattering, beefy pink, is set on the right with the least servant on the left. To my dismay, Margaret is always portrayed as standing on my own right, a corrective to any notions I may from time to time have entertained about the dominance of the male.

Nothing is spared, from white children being wheeled in push-chairs by black nannies, to the visitors—who can be recognized by their cameras—and gaudily-chasubled clergymen at their offices. Aerial diagrams of the hospital buildings are favourite subjects, the buildings lying on their sides and transparently showing much that goes on inside them. There are patients, wrapped in scarlet blankets, lying in the wards, and the senior staff house has always cooking, in a vast frying-pan, an abundance of delicious food.

Formal lessons are forbidden since African education came under the care of the Minister of Native Affairs; only by handwork and crafts may the children's time be occupied—except, that is, for singing lessons. These take up a disproportionate amount of the morning in maddening repetitions of rhythm-songs which have no beginning and no end save the closing of school for the day. Mrs Nsibande herself invented the school song, defiant, swelling with rebellion against the taking away of the mission schools :

Johnson School, Johnson School; we shall fight until we die!
We shall never, never lose; we shall fight until we die!

It was as unsuitable as it could very well be, but it was composed, like the 'Marseillaise' and the 'Star Spangled Banner,' from the heart. We felt we should have been very wrong indeed to question its sentiments; anyhow we agreed pretty thoroughly with them.

Not long after the play-centre had opened, a high official of the Government turned up, partly to look around the hospital and partly to assure us of an official warmth and benevolence in high places of which, it must be confessed, we had entertained doubts. He was expansive and persuasive and through a prolonged and faintly embarrassing tea-time made protestations of goodwill which it would have been churlish to doubt. Seeing that all resistance was at an end, he stood up and took a turn about the room, gazing out through the window. Across the lawn he saw the round, black heads of the children in the play-centre. 'What is that place?' he inquired.

'It's the sch— the play-centre,' we replied.

'How very nice!' He was animated, really interested for the first time.

'Would you care to have a look at the children's work, sir?'

We moved down to the building. I sensed trouble coming, but was not certain what form it would take. The children's work was genuinely admired. 'And can they sing?' asked the official. I froze in prescience of Mrs Nsibande's reply.

'Oh, yes, sir.' She was so happy and anyhow there was nothing I could do. I stared at the floor and hummed a little tune to myself, and worked my toes into knots inside my shoes, pretending all the time that I was invisible; perhaps the children's diction would be so poor that the words could not be distinguished?

But Mrs Nsibande's elocution was as sound as the rest of her teaching and every word fell crystal clear from those innocent lips upon my ears and the ears and senses of the official.

'We shall fight until we die.' The children's eyes were half-closed in the beauty of the moment. 'We shall never, never, lose . . .'

CHAPTER NINE

Choose Your Own Cure

I

TO all the skills and advantages of modern medicine our patients brought an attitude of wary scepticism. It seemed to us astonishing that any one could doubt the efficacy of rational treatment, the relief of good nursing and the security of coming under reasonably competent medical care. Yet our Zulu neighbours did doubt all these things in an open, unashamed way and without much tact to cushion the blows thus rained upon our pride. There were a lot of things wrong with us, of course; we were young, white and foreign; we had no knowledge of the language and, presumably therefore, of the disorders which our patients considered to be peculiar to themselves. It is likely, too, that we showed the same lack of consideration for their viewpoint as they showed towards ours, and with as little refinement of manners.

In addition to the reticence that any one might feel towards putting themselves in the hands of a young, inexperienced doctor, there was a strong sense among the patients that their diseases were African diseases and thus hidden from our foreign eyes. After all, it is human enough to believe our problems to be unique. We speak of *our* gall-bladders, *our* stomachs, *our* appendices, as if we owned them like so many lap-dogs to be pampered and fed. We think of our nerves and our systems as peculiar and inalienable, into the hidden working of which our old family doctor might have gained insight, but to which his young assistant is blind and insensitive. And this sense of possession which we have towards our bodies, goes very deep; so deep that our happiness largely depends on their wholeness and health. To lose an organ, even one which, like the kidney, does not show, leaves us with an inexplicable sense of loss. To lose some visible part—an eye or a limb—is one of the sternest tests to which our human nature can be put.

Thus, most diseases which patients recognized in themselves were at first considered to be in some way peculiarly African. 'You wouldn't have been able to help,' said the women, recounting the deaths of their children, 'the child had one of the sicknesses of the people.' The symptoms they described, diarrhœa and vomitting or coughing with high fever, indicated nothing very mysterious yet the belief persisted that such symptoms were an exclusively African privilege.

Even in later years, when the logic of results had convinced many that medical science is no respecter of persons, there remained disorders about which still clung the old, proprietary feeling. These People's Diseases were not entirely, as they might have been expected to be, those in which we had little success. It was true that our repeated failure to relieve mental disorders meant that many of these and in particular the hysterias of young women, remained for a long time outside our province. Quite common troubles also, intestinal upsets in babies and breast abscesses in nursing mothers, were included among African diseases, sometimes with disastrous results. Perversely, the one condition which we saw that really was limited to Africans—a spontaneous amputation of the little toes of unknown origin—was brought regularly to us for treatment.

Year by year we saw the line shift in our favour that divided the spheres of influence of the medicine-man and the doctor. Pellagra, a nutritional deficiency-state with an unsightly skin rash and mental confusion, became a hospital disease about 1947. I was first made aware of this change of outlook when a man brought his son, disfigured and demented, to the out-patients. To my suggestion that the boy be admitted he was unexpectedly pliant. 'Yes,' he said, 'you may admit him to hospital; the doctors have learnt how to treat Zulu diseases now.'

It was allowed that for some conditions at least our methods were superior to those of the medicine-men, but although our medicines were admittedly good—so ran the argument—it did not follow that we really understood the needs of our patients. We were obviously deficient in comprehension when it came to the subtleties of magic and bewitchment, since we discounted these powerful forces with a haughty air or, worse, with laughter.

We came slowly to understand that our patients, passing without any apparent sense of disloyalty or guilt from the hospital to the medicine-man, were really asking two different things of their advisers in fields so far apart that no inconsistency was implied by this extraordinary shuttle-service. Of the doctor was asked relief of symptom at the least, and cure if possible; the medicine-man stood more in the role of pathologist. 'Why was I ill?' they ask him. 'Who put this sickness upon me and my family?'

It all depended on how you viewed sickness, whether as a deviation from the normal workings of the body under the influence of bacteria or unknown agents as in cancer, or whether as a consequence of evil influences put upon a man by his enemies. Many of our patients leaned towards the latter view and, having received as much relief as we could offer, went to the medicine-man for him to tidy up those aspects of their malady which we, obtusely as it seemed, had failed to recognize or treat.

Since this after-treatment would include at least the administration of ruthless emetics and violent purges, we not only had to get our patients fit to return home, but also to withstand this searching test of their recovery. In a few tragic cases we learnt of children who, discharged well one day, were dead by the close of the next, having been thus cleansed of lingering evil.

Because we did not accept magic and witchcraft as causative of the suffering and discomforts of our patients, we were often unable to answer their fundamental questions in terms comprehensible to them. This put us at a disadvantage before the medicine-men who could and did accept the connection and whose explanations so well accorded with the prejudice of their patients. Magic is so intensely real to those who believe in its power both to save and to destroy; it seems to explain so much that otherwise, in the absence of knowledge, is wholly inexplicable. Death-rates were so high, and the assaults of sickness so universal that it was not difficult—where nothing was known of bacteria and very little more of food values—to conclude that these calamities were the result of bewitchment.

But it would be unjust to suggest that more than a minority still clung to the traditional beliefs of their fathers about magic and witchcraft. There was so much solid good sense in the attitudes of so many parents to their sick children; so much desire among the womenfolk for safe childbirth in hospital; so great thankfulness among the elderly when they could rest their aching bones against piled hospital pillows, that it was evident that the old attitudes were losing their hold. Where we failed, in hopeless cancers or in chronic ailments, the spirit-world would again be invoked, but often only in despair which prompted fond relatives to leave no avenue unexplored which might lead to a last-minute restoration of their sufferer's health. When this happened, European know-alls were ready to point a finger: 'You see, doc? They're a primitive lot at heart, and given half a chance, always go back to their old ways; you'll never change them.'

Yet I fancy that the return to the magician owed more to love than to fear; more to a desire to help in an extremity than to the persistence of superstition. All varieties of quacks and herbal cranks flourish in our own society on the edges of the well-tilled fields of medicine. To some extent their continued existence, like that of the tribal medicine-man, must be laid at our door who do not know enough and whose medical philosophy is too small to embrace, in addition to the body's ills, the needs of the sick soul.

2

So much has been written about witch-doctors, of which so little will bear examination, that it were better that the title, with its associations of orgiastic ceremony, black magic and human sacrifice, should be forgotten. It is desirable that we should assume a less hysterical attitude towards these men and women—for many of them are women—and stop thinking of them as devoid of human sympathies and given over entirely to bloodshed and cruelty. There has indeed been cruelty in which these practitioners have played a leading part; even to-day in ritual murders among the Basuto and recently in the bestialities of the Kenya emergency, they have been in evidence. For much that has occurred they can neither be excused nor suffered to go free, yet their evil has been manifested in societies themselves cruel, unthinking and brutish. It is not comparable with the foulness of the Nazi prison camps where men, who had behind them the heritage of centuries of Christendom, turned their backs on all mercy and all humanity to become pagans anew.

Beyond the ignorance, and the unquestionably bad consequences of that ignorance, there is yet to be recognized in these medicine-men a certain rough integrity and logic. Believing as they do in the profound influence of the ancestors upon the living members of the clan, they act rationally enough and in a sufficiently disciplined way. They have served an apprenticeship and learned their craft at the feet of its masters; they have in their make up both compassion and tenderness; watching their influence decline before the new learning, they have often behaved with humility and dignity.

In any case it would be inaccurate to lump together under any single title, men as diverse as Sam Molife and Juba Sithole. Molife was a Diviner, a familiar of the ancestral spirits, a trainer of other Diviners and a man of eminence in his profession. Sithole, at the other end of the scale, practised as a herbalist and itinerant therapist; he was humble and self-effacing where Molife was confident. Both were friendly towards us and used the hospital themselves when they or their dependents were ill.

Molife brought his child, Mashobi, to hospital with her back already bent by tuberculosis and her legs cold, blue and paralysed from damage to the spinal cord. She was put on a plaster bed and for the next two years grew up with us, her legs becoming warmer and increasing little by little in power as she lay long days and nights as flat as her energetic mind and the plaster's restraining straps would hold her. But recovery was incomplete and when her father came to take her home with him for a few days, it seemed as if all hope was gone of her ever being able to get about again. So often such requests were but polite ways of asking for medical treatment to be discontinued, and Molife must have known how we should react, because he began by apologizing for disturbing us with requests which he knew could not be welcome. Nevertheless he begged us to let him try his own methods for a while, since Mashobi's progress under our hands was so slow. 'I've a goat I should like Mashobi to see,' he added shyly.

'A goat?'

'Yes, it is our custom to kill a goat on these occasions.'

'Couldn't you bring the goat down here?' I asked.

'There is also my sister, the child's aunt, who has come for the ceremony.'

'Couldn't she come too?'

Molife looked uncomfortable. 'She is a Diviner, like me, and would like to have the child at home for the ceremony.'

'Could I bring the goat and Mashobi's aunt down in the truck, so that you can work here?'

'Yes,' he said doubtfully, 'but she might not like it.'

I realized he was referring to the aunt. 'Let's go and see,' I suggested.

At his home he left me in the truck while he went to speak with his sister. He did not reappear for nearly half an hour, and when he did it was to go round to the back of the house and return, leading a splendid white billy-goat. He lifted the goat into the back of the truck and, with his sister who was dressed in the full uniform of her profession, climbed into the cab beside me.

Getting the goat into the ward was less trouble than I had expected but its arrival caused a great stir; Mashobi was tremendously excited, her face round, bright and animated.

'If we could just take Mashobi up home for a little while?' Molife asked again. It seemed reasonable, and by now it was certain that he would return her to hospital at the close of the ceremony.

'May I come as well?' I asked.

Molife smiled courteously. 'We should like you to,' he said.

We moved off down the drive, Molife and I in front, the child, the aunt and the goat in the rear.

Back at the home, I helped Molife place his daughter in her plaster cast on the ground in front of the house and then stood to one side while Molife went inside. When he came out again, he was transformed; his shirt was gone, replaced by strings of beads and little brass bells which jangled as he walked. He was still wearing khaki shorts, but over them he had put on his loin-covering of monkeys' tails and strips of hide; round his ankles were tied dry, whispering nuts; in one hand he carried a bead-encrusted knobkerry, in the other the cowtail switch of the Diviner.

His wife, matter-of-fact in a cotton print dress and tidy shoes, came out of the house after him, bearing a drum; she sat down against the wall watching the slow gathering of a little crowd of inquisitive neighbours. A second woman joined the aunt; both wore bead-aprons and carried switches; their hair hung down over their eyes like the fringe of a sheepdog. Molife turned round a few times, slowly, his arms outstretched, and began a jerky, rhythmic song; the drum took up the time and the two women slid into the dance, coldly, casual as plain-clothes policemen.

To the tap of the drum they started to shuffle, forward a few paces and then back again, treading the dust into little clouds about their whispering ankles. The crowd echoed the quickening beat of the drum, clapping with their hands, sharply, accurately reinforcing the rhythm. Molife's feet lifted and fell, thudding on the baked earth, stamping to the time of the dance; sweat gathered on his face and ran down the side of his nose. Momentarily he stood, exalted between the women, his body tense and still, his breathing harsh from exertion; first his shoulders and then his whole frame began trembling, setting the nuts chattering about his ankles and the little bells tinkling. Muscles whose names it had been an effort to learn in the dissecting room came into individual prominence, standing out under the tight, sweating skin, dancing for a moment their own, quivering measure. With a cry, his sticks whirling, he went back into the women's step and as abruptly, stopped chanting. The dance came to an end.

He fetched the goat then and, leading it by the horns, presented it to his daughter. Speaking in Sesutho, which I could not follow, he intoned some sentences with the proficiency of a priest and then, drawing a wire skewer from his belt, he raised it high in the air. It was the moment of sacrifice, a moment solemn and impressive, evoking all the countless acts of bloodshed with which men, since the dawn of time, have striven to make their requests known before the blunt sense of their gods. The skewer flashed down and bent, miserably failing to penetrate the thick hide of the goat.

It was horribly embarrassing, like a soloist drying up at a concert, and I felt deeply for Molife at that moment. He skewered the wretched animal to death in a less dramatic manner and went again into the house to fetch a carving knife.

After the botched-up sacrifice, his dissection of the body with that gross knife was a technical triumph which left me gasping with admiration. Under other circumstances, and with a different training he might have achieved brilliance as an operator. Only the really competent could have removed that goat's gall-bladder as he did, so neatly, precisely and in so short a time; it was nothing that the goat was dead, the mastery was indisputable. He took the limp organ, ran some of the bile over his hand and rubbed it with extreme tenderness over the poor, bent spine, down the wasted, chill legs, murmuring softly as he did so in unmistakable love and grief. When all the bile was used up, he put the gall-bladder to his lips and blew it up; then tying off the neck with a cord, he hung the pink, damp balloon round Mashobi's neck.

The drum began again; the Diviners came forward and the dance was repeated. He sang in Zulu this time, a wild, disjointed song broken by the gasps of his breathing, but I realized that it was a praise song I was intended to hear and, if I could, to understand. He chanted of his daughter's illness that had so suddenly and mysteriously weakened her legs; of how she had lain long, long in the hospital; of how much better she was—I wished we had deserved that part a bit more—of the hospital's understanding which had allowed him to treat his daughter in his own way; of his hope that the hospital might last for ever. Suddenly he came over to me: 'That's all,' he said in English. 'We would like you to take Mashobi back now.'

It was another two years before the child was able to get about, holding on to the other cots in the ward. By then, the softening of her spine was overcome, but there was some residual damage to the spinal cord, which meant that any increase in muscular power must be very slow, and the final result in all probability less than perfect. A few days before Mashobi's fourth Christmas in hospital, her mother claimed her and took her away to Johannesburg. Nearly three years afterwards I met Molife in the road. 'What news have you of Mashobi?' I asked.

'I've seen her; she can walk quite well in her irons,' he said, pleased. 'She's quite grown up now.'

It was good to know that her mother had done this for her and that the child had hope of a reasonably normal life; it was good, too, to have experienced the simple grace of that praise song from another man who cared about the same things as I did, however much our methods were at variance.

3

Juba Sithole, the herbalist, expressed his concern for my health as I went past his bed one day in paroxysms of hay fever. He was recovering from pneumonia and felt well enough that day to regale himself in all the trappings of his office, which he wore over his pyjamas, horns filled with medicines, pouches and shoulder bags and, on his head, a fur hat.

'That's a bad cold you've got there, doctor,' he remarked.

I do not know any word in Zulu for hay fever and was unable to correct his diagnosis. 'Can you cure it for me?' I asked.

'Of course I can,' he said.

I sneezed again, and forgot the old man's words. What, anyhow, could he offer me?

After his treatment was completed he was discharged and I did not even think of him again until a fortnight later, in a blinding thunderstorm with rods of rain lashing the earth and thunder rocking the buildings, I saw him through the out-patient door. He was walking quite unhurriedly up the path, soaked from the crown of his fur hat to the soles of his horny feet. Thinking of his but recently healed lungs, I pulled him inside out of the rain as quickly as I could. Nurse and I wrung him out and tried to warm him up over a paraffin stove, attentions which he endured with a distracted air, passive and uncomplaining.

'I've come to treat your cold,' he announced when we had him more or less dry again.

From the satchel which he carried over his bent, old shoulders he brought a roll of cloth, unfolded it and laid out an assortment of roots and fragments of bark on the top of my desk. 'These'—he pointed to some woody radishes—'are for sneezing; this'—he took up a piece of bark—'is for expelling the bile, and here are medicines for chest pain and fever.'

I took up the radishes and one or two other of the fresher-looking objects, as I was clearly expected to make a choice from among the medicines. 'I'll have these, please,' I said, adding from memories of the cathartic experience of my patients, 'but don't bother about the bile-expeller.'

He asked for fire and a cooking pot but it was already late and we gave him lodging for the night, promising him the necessary materials in the morning. He must have risen early, for by seven o'clock he came to give me a gin bottle full of his medicine, still warm from its infusion.

'How do I take it?' I asked, fearing his reply; so many Zulu remedies are given as enemas.

'Oh, I don't know,' he answered vaguely, 'how do you usually take medicines?'

The old formula came to my aid : 'Two teaspoonfuls three times a day?' I suggested.

'That will do very well.' He seemed pleased by the idea, for the originality of which I'm afraid he gave me full and undeserved credit.

I solemnly drank the first dose in his presence, pulling an appropriate face; it tasted like a Scottish peat-bog, but it might have been much worse. Perhaps if I had duly drunk the whole bottle-full I should not now be a continuing sufferer from hay-fever. Possibly I have only myself to blame for having left the bottle on the dispensary shelf, whence it disappeared over a few days. I hope it cured somebody of something and that the old herbalist's work was not entirely wasted by my ingratitude.

4

Out of the slow but emphatic change of heart in favour of modern medicine that is taking place, the doctors are doing very well. But if these are boom times for doctors, they are also halcyon days for the sellers of patent medicines. Theirs is a market any one might envy, and the numerous brands available indicate a healthy level of business. Patent medicines are relatively cheap, cheaper certainly than going to a private doctor or a medicine-man; they are freely available at the trading stores, and they can be bought and consumed in abundance without the pusillanimous ethics of doctors to moderate their dosage.

A certain grudging credit must be accorded to the sellers of these remedies. They have had their difficulties, of which the chief has been to guide illiterate customers in their choice of the appropriate medicine. One firm provides an enamel sign suitable for fixing to the counter. It is predominantly yellow, about two feet by three feet in size, and shows a human figure in silhouette. All around the edge are little red squares in which are described, for the benefit of those who can read, the properties

11. *Mother and child*

12. *Mixing beer before the wedding*

of each mixture advertised. From each of the squares an arrow points to the central figure and in particular to some organ or region of the body which will be benefited by the medicine whose number appears in the red square. Thus, from number 8 (backache and kidney pills) an arrow passes to the kidneys which are revealed as brilliant yellow beans in a black lake. From numbers 13 and 14 the conjoined arrows reach out to a painfully distended bladder. The intestine is the haunt of worms, long and lumbrical, for which the antidote is number 22.

One of the traders, who occupied a seat on the hospital Board for many years, had a virtual monopoly in another series of medicines whose marketing lacked even the crude honesty of the enamel chart. These were sold in little bottles and were designed for hanging round the neck rather than for consumption, their function being to protect against spells, poisons and magic. The phials contained powders, slips of bark and portions of decaying animal matter said to be the fat of pythons or fragments of crocodile liver. It was an unseemly, cynical trade, but sales were at no time very brisk and I have an idea they became worse as the hospital grew in influence.

Dutch folk-remedies, mostly in the form of drops sold in cylindrical one-ounce bottles, are also popular. They are designed for the use of country Afrikaners and are emotionally of a piece with ox wagons, volks-pele and treks as part of Voortrekker culture. But they find a wide custom among Africans where, although some are drunk according to the instructions on the label, more are hung in amulets round the necks of babies.

Not to be outdone, chemists in the neighbouring market towns put up pills and mixtures of their own devising and of brilliant colour. These pills are marketed as 'Extra Strong Native Pills' satisfying a craving for purgation which I neither share nor understand. Epsom salts are sold in one-ounce packets; croton oil and castor oil—or fierce mixtures of the two —are freely available to the most ignorant of mothers for use on their children. Caustic soda can be bought over the counter in one-pound tins, and the beautiful orange crystals of potassium bichromate, which is a powerful kidney poison, are laid out on trays for the public to buy as it pleases. It is not surprising that fatalities occur; poisoning with potassium bichromate is becoming increasingly common and I recall a man spending a very unpleasant fortnight after his wife—it must be accepted that she was not without a legitimate grudge against him—had given him an enema of concentrated caustic soda. There have been three or four known deaths from worm mixtures, which may destroy the liver-cells, and at least one in a European from a dose of salts taken in the early savable hours of intestinal obstruction. But these are the rarities and the accidents; more serious is the delay occasioned by faith in these remedies. The precious hours may all be dissipated while anxious mothers wait for the medicine to work.

In addition to those purchased over the counter, tons of bottles, jars, packets and phials are brought in weekly by post to the eager recipients who have replied to the vendors' advertisements. These pamphlets are sent in sheafs to teachers, nurses, high-school children, members of school boards, clergymen, B.A.s, and any one else who is believed to be able to read. They contain colourful descriptions of symptoms that the readers can be depended upon to have felt, and order forms which promise free worm draught for introducers of five new customers.

Medicine by post is the preserve of African vendors, many of whom reach affluence on a flood tide of bladder-mixture and gripe-water. Having a special knowledge of their customers' prejudices and requirements, they include among more reputable mixtures a strange hotch-potch of complexion lightening creams, hair straighteners and love-philtres.

'Our medicines speak for themselves in a person's illness. When everything else has failed, don't forget that all medicines are not dug in the same place. The opportunity we are giving you is unique, so don't you let it pass you by without utilizing it. Grasp the opportunity! Don't ask another party to do things for you! Now it's up to you, African!'

Indeed the opportunity does seem great : one single remedy can both 'Strengthen reproduction *and* clean the Bladder' for the moderate sum of ten shillings and sixpence, while the next on the list 'clears the bowel both ways . . .; will take out all beetles should they be present in the bowels. Good for both men and women!' Good indeed, whatever the price, for harbouring beetles in the bowel is not unnaturally considered a grave disorder.

These postal physicians are aware, to an extent that many doctors might emulate with benefit, of the emotional and psychological stresses which give rise to symptoms in their patients. Treatment is offered for headaches, for the 'facilitation of clear thinking' and there is 'The eye-opener; this is for eyes which are always oozing tears and do not want to be exposed to the sun'—all common neurotic symptoms.

A 'Good medicine' is offered for 'Preventing evil-spirits when in the midst of strangers. It also dignifies you and makes people afraid of you.'

Nor is appearance neglected : 'A lean wife hasn't the smallest shadow of dignity! Here's the medicine to restore that lost respect in the eyes of your friends.' For twenty shillings can be purchased 'They-Follow-Him Perfume' which is good 'for young people anxious to look attractive.' Fertilizer for the beard, 'for young men who love a flourishing beard' is only fifteen shillings the bottle.

'Remember,' the pamphlet ends on a tender note. 'Remember, we are your dear friends, so keep no secrets from us; we are out to help you.'

There was also the brief and glorious age when Tonic Wine was introduced into the district. Wines are not generally permitted in Reserve Territories, although it is possible for men of sufficient standing to obtain permits for the purchase of liquor. From these regulations wines with a small quantity of iron added and marketed as Tonic Wines were exempt. The good news of their coming reached the police camp first, and first among the force was Sergeant Ndima who made what haste he could to find out for himself. He bought two bottles and, sitting under the shade of the gum trees opposite the church, drank first the one bottle and then the second before the tonic effect caught up with him and laid him flat.

Later, though less dramatic, sessions with the wines caused a stirring of conscience in some of the traders whose supplies were slower in coming forward or who had missed the original boom. For a while only Outsiders sold tonic wines and their slow reintroduction as the circle of these grew has been marked by no scandal.

Against the formidable alliance of vintners, magicians, pharmacists, *parfumiers,* medicine-men and business representatives, the going was bound to be hard. The wonder was that any one bothered about the doctor at all. But the slow, critical common sense of Africa told in the end and the first sign of the change was a commercial traveller grumbling in the bar that he sold less medicines in a year than he formerly sold in a month. I stood him a beer to make it up to him.

CHAPTER TEN

Surgery Against Odds

I

'YOU can't do it here,' Thandizwe was patronizing, 'I want you to send me down to a town hospital.'

We were new still and my pride was touched; the peacock in me spoke defiantly : 'Of course we can take it off for you.'

'You won't kill me?'

'Of course not!'

'Sure?' He was softening.

'No, no; of course we shan't.'

'But you'll hurt me.'

'You won't know anything about it; we shall put you to sleep.'

Thandizwe looked at his gangrenous leg, fingering the numb, sloppy skin. 'All right,' he said, 'if you want to, you can.' He was bored with the discussion, tired from sleepless nights and fiery, stinking days in the company of that sloughing flesh which was all that remained of his chances of the future. His other leg had been amputated a year before, and who will employ a black man without legs?

Margaret and I looked through the available instruments; there were the six artery forceps we had brought with us, a good scalpel and a few retractors and tissue forceps that had come down to us from some long-dead practitioner or insolvent nursing-home. There was no bone saw. Thandizwe had been about right; we could at a pinch amputate his leg, but it was very doubtful if we ought to with such meagre equipment.

An amateur interest in woodwork and romantic notions of the future had together ensured my having a well filled tool box in which was a saw which would cut as well, I supposed, as any saw in shining steel. It could, if need arose, be boiled no less effectively. It turned out to be too large for the sterilizer, but the vegetable saucepan would hold it, and the matron, who acted as theatre sister, served it up on the trolley without comment.

The operation itself was completed without incident, for limb amputations, while associated with tremendous strain on the patient's faith in him-

self and in his future, are at the same time among the more elementary
surgical exercises. The saw lost most of the golden varnish which had made
its wonderfully functional handle such a joy to hold, but that was the
only casualty, for Thandizwe's leg healed to a useful conical stump on
which he was quickly about again.

It has generally been difficult to get good artificial limbs, or indeed any
artificial portions of the body of any kind. Even those who have a simple
but well-fitting prosthesis are inclined to leave them, like National Health
Service dentures, in the bathroom cupboard. There must be many homes
where leg irons and supports for limbs weakened by poliomyelitis are lying
in mint condition while children shuffle on calloused hips or are borne
on the backs of their mothers. One leper, scornful of the pylon limbs which
a generous government had given him when he had lost his own, made himself two more to his liking out of paraffin tins. He stuffed the cone-shaped
legs with old rags and painted them with the yellowish-brown paint used
all over the world to decorate public buildings. The new legs were short
but serviceable and he felt more normal on their brown brevity than on
an iron paten.

Artificial eyes are a continuing source of disappointment to their wearers,
as they are expected to restore lost vision as much as damaged appearance.
After two years a man applied for a disability grant, complaining that
he had worn his glass-eye day and night and still the thing did not work.

Deformities and disfigurements arouse the same interest as in any society,
shorn only of the elegant restraints on the curiosity of more sophisticated
communities. There is no intention to inflict pain in the long stares which
replace the furtive glances of our own squeamish age, nor is there conscious
malice in the laughter evoked by the antics of the mad. Dwarfs, hunchbacks
and simpletons leer, gibbering through the pages of our nursery books;
they were an inescapable part of the life of four centuries ago and still
hold their ancient sway in modern Zululand. Often I have rebuked the
laughter of bystanders when some misshapen man or woman has come
for the help I could never give, but in my aroused pity was nothing comparable with the fundamental acceptance of these curiosities that the Zulus
showed by marrying and giving in marriage, men and women of the
simplest minds and the most grossly deformed bodies. One woman of my
acquaintance, half of whose face is grotesquely enlarged and caricatured
by a tumour of the lymphatic vessels, is the mother of four children, while
more than one patient with readily curable disfigurement has declined
even the simplest surgery, content with a face that was as the Lord
made it.

Nevertheless, albinism—the absence of pigment in the skin, hair and eyes —is a sore trial to those upon whom it is visited. It is a disorder appearing in families, transmitted by a recessive gene which jumps generations and may then be manifest in several children of the same marriage. Dissimilar twins may be born, the one normally coloured, the other waxy-white. These unfortunate children bear through a lifetime the burden of their deficient pigmentation—a sore, dry skin unprotected from sunburn, liable to eczema, tender and irritant. Local tradition says that albinos are bad-tempered, but it is not to be wondered at that these children, who are called monkeys by their fellows, become hypersensitive and irritable. Yet they, too, men and women alike, take their full part in family life and, once the childhood hurt is soothed, are by no means condemned to lifelong solitude and unhappiness.

In former times, and nowadays among the less educated people, it was usual to stretch the ear lobes. The ears were pierced at puberty and stretched by the introduction of reeds, one by one, until the lobe could carry two-inch ornaments of coloured wood. In fights these dangling lobes frequently get torn, for it is easy to slip a finger into the ready made circle and rip the flesh with a quick downward movement. Repair of these torn ears is an elementary surgical exercise which, if successful, is warmly appreciated. In recent years an increasing number of people have come asking for their stretched ear-lobes to be restored to the original shape. There seem to be two reasons for this : first, and to me rather less than convincing, because the woman wishes to dress in western style and attend church ; second, because standards of beauty are changing. Two mission doctors of my acquaintance have, from the frailty of these motives, de-clined to carry out this purely cosmetic operation, and I might have had my own doubts about its propriety could I not call upon experience of a sharp rebuke I once received from a plastic surgeon. I had said something sillier than usual about face-lifting. 'Why shouldn't we help a woman to look her best?' he had retorted. So I accepted ear-sewing as part of my normal operative range and found satisfaction in the not wholly easy art of getting the two sides equal and of natural appearance.

Circumcision ceased to be practised among the Zulus in Shakas' time, and has not been reintroduced, but among Hlubi's Basutho it is still a universal custom, associated with puberty rites and initiation into tribal lore. I have never been permitted to see the methods used by the elders, and from that tribal freemasonry there is no leak of information. What is more remarkable is that we have never had a single youth brought to us for any complication of the operation, nor have we seen the bad results of an improperly conducted circumcision. Whatever methods the elders use, they can boast results which few young surgeons, for all their training, could equal.

2

Even among the earlier patients there was less formal opposition to surgical operations than might have been expected, although we were never without those who could not summon up sufficient courage to submit themselves to the torments of surgery. Rather, it was delay in coming to the doctor at all that crippled our endeavours and stayed our hands. 'It will take you ten years to get an acute surgical emergency into hospital in time to deal with it successfully,' was the warning of one experienced surgeon, and though this proved an exaggeration, such cases were rarities until at eight years we did admit a case of intestinal obstruction in time to relieve it and have the pleasure of seeing the patient recover.

It is not difficult to imagine why this should be. Catastrophic physical occurrences are especially likely to be ascribed to magical causes, to the secret administration of poison or, at any rate, to events outside the normal range of experience. Apart from the family discussions which are desirable at times of crisis, it is more than likely that the medicine-man will be given the first opportunity to treat the condition since it falls so obviously within his province. The doctor's hope of being called in reasonable time lies mainly with the patient. If his suffering is intense enough, his insistence on relief may frighten the relatives into speedy action; but only too often the patient is too preoccupied by pain to exert himself for his own salvation.

Hope dwindles after twelve hours' obstruction of the small intestine, and after twenty-four hours the outlook is unrelievedly bad. When the large intestine is involved there is a little more grace, but only a little, still to be measured in anxious hours rather than philosophical days. All our early cases of obstruction died, like a child of one year, even while we sought to obtain the father's permission for operation, others on the operating table, others again after a valiant struggle of several days to restore lost body-fluids once the organic obstruction had been relieved. Each case we lost firmly reinforced the accepted truth that, if you went into hospital, and particularly if you had an operation, you would die. It was all too true; you did.

The same understandable but equally disastrous delays were met with in conditions requiring cold, formal surgery. Cancers were often pathetically late in presenting for treatment, with all hope of relief swallowed up in delays and futile therapy at home. Septic fingers came when the pus had slyly tracked even beyond the boundaries of the hand and up into the crannies of the forearm. Eyes with once relievable ulceration of the cornea, came when they were blind, agonizing balls of fire.

But slowly there was an improvement. Apart from the emergencies of midwifery which were the first to come with reasonable haste, cases of severe injury were brought intelligently and rapidly for hospital treatment. Perhaps this was because their origin was so much more understandable; a knife wound starts no philosophical train of reasoning, but calls rather for decisive action. There is the added incentive also of vengeance on the attacker through the processes of the law. The latter, less worthy motive, gave us continual trouble. From the complainant's point of view the case was very nearly as exciting when for a scratch as for a spear-thrust through the bowels, and both came to hospital with equal solemnity. Our refusal to admit the trivialities was looked upon as evidence of our failure to understand the real issues involved in an assault case, for admission to hospital materially strengthened the chances of impressing the Native Commissioner —or so it was argued.

In former days the usual weapon of assault was the heavy headed knobkerry which, brought down with ferocity on a neighbour's skull or whacked across his shins, was capable of laying him out for a longish time but only comparatively rarely killed him. Latterly the knife is becoming a more favoured instrument and the revolver era cannot be far away, having dawned already in the cities where vice, in common with education, is more advanced along the road to civilization. A knobkerry wound on the head will break the bone and render the recipient unconscious, but may cause no outward tearing of the scalp. Before I knew this I very nearly overlooked a serious skull fracture which might have led to permanent disablement or even death, simply by taking lightly a head injury in which the scalp was to all appearances uninjured. As he remained deeply unconscious I decided to explore the region of the injury and, if necessary, to decompress the brain. On incising the scalp there was an efflux of old blood and it was evident that the injury was more severe than I had thought. Wiping away clots I found I was looking at the *inside* surface of a portion of skull more than two inches across. This fragment of bone had completely separated itself from its membranous coverings and had rotated through a full 180° to turn inside out, and this entirely below an intact scalp. The scalp itself is not a yielding structure and in its turning, the bone must have found space at the expense of the more elastic brain substance. The patient was none the worse for his experience, making a good recovery after spending a week or so in a not altogether surprising coma.

Farmer-neighbours and other wiseacres, observing the good recoveries that follow such severe head injuries, believe that these are due to the 'thick skulls' that Africans are supposed to possess. It is a convenient belief because it explains, by a sort of emotional free-association, the difficulties they experience in getting African servants to carry out their orders, as if these were absorbed, not through the normal channels of hearing, but direct through the bone to the brain. The actual explanation of the apparent superiority of Africans to Europeans in their capacity to stand head injuries is less flattering to the Europeans and thus less emotionally satisfying. The difference lies in the type of head injury the two groups commonly sustain. The African stick-injury is a small force applied with great speed to one area of the brain. It bruises the underlying brain locally, but leaves the rest of the organ more or less undisturbed. European head injuries, on the other hand, are commonly the result of motor accidents in which the head, with all the momentum of the body's weight behind it, strikes the dashboard, the windscreen or a brick wall, causing a swirling tumult of the whole brain sufficient to kill the patient outright.

3

The endurance of pain in many who are seriously injured is an inspiration in itself. An old man from the Mbathas, living in the thorn country almost on the banks of the Tugela river, received a spear-thrust through his abdomen. His family took him on a sledge as far as the Norwegian Mission Hospital seven miles from his home, where he was admitted for the night. As there was at the time no doctor at the hospital, the sister in charge drove him down to us as soon as it was light next morning, a forty mile journey over one of the roughest roads. He was shocked and ill when he was admitted, with clear evidence of internal injuries, but he never made a moan nor even winced as we carried him from the ambulance. At operation he had four perforations of his bowel—it is a surgical truism that if you find an uneven number of holes you have probably missed the one that will kill your patient—which we closed readily enough and returned him to bed with the number of rubber tubes and suspended bottles that is customary in such cases. He did very well and walked home a few weeks later.

Obtaining permission for operations was the occasion for the onset of acute panic in many who would, unasked, have been satisfied to put their trust in the doctor's judgment. We behaved conscientiously in all cases where deformity would result from our ministrations, the removal of hopelessly injured eyes or teeth, the amputations or where there was a serious risk to life in the operation. In acute emergencies our mode of asking more nearly resembled commands and a brisk assurance that we were going to 'put things right inside' was seldom met with protest or refusal. It was difficult to steer a just course between being dictatorial and, by overweening correctness, plunging the patient into a crisis of indecision which might end all hope of a successful outcome. That we have been wrong from time to time is certain, advising operation in cases where the patient's refusal has been rewarded, not by the predicted disaster, but by uninterrupted recovery. But we have been right, too, and have been forced to watch patients walk away with still operable cancers because we have failed to persuade them of the necessity for surgical relief.

Finally, we are all at liberty to die in our own way rather than the doctor's, let him be never so enlightened and we the most ignorant of mortals.

We asked Mrs Mpanza, about one o'clock in the morning, for permission to do a Cæsarian section on her for her first delivery. The theatre staff was on hand; two doctors were preparing for the operation, the sterilizers were boiling and the trolley had gone along to the ward to fetch her. The display of medical quixotism was too much for the poor woman, who refused at the last minute to get on to the trolley. 'I can't give you permission; you must ask my father if you want to operate on me.'

We were shaken. 'But you can't *refuse*,' we chorused.

But Mrs Mpanza had gone numb and still with emotion like a hare in the headlights. 'You'll have to ask my father,' she repeated.

We knew her home was sixteen miles away at least, and over these roads the journey would take a long time; too long, perhaps, for that feebly beating fœtal heart which was already in danger of fading for ever away.

Urgently we pleaded. 'You *must* agree; you have got to have this operation if your baby is to be born alive!' But her reply was the same: Go and ask my father; if he says so, you can operate on me.'

We sent for the ambulance driver and dispatched him into the darkness to find the father at all costs, whatever he was doing, and bring him back. We turned again to listen through the warm wall of the mother's belly to the gentle beating of the child's heart. It had improved; the fright we had given her had sent her out of labour, which meant that we had a respite while father was brought. The woman, reprieved, went to sleep; we returned to our beds, full of anxiety.

It was nearly dawn before the driver returned with an expansive father, clearly flattered by so much attention being paid to his views about anything. 'Of course you must do as you think fit.' He was magnificent, generously granting his daughter for the sacrifices of the operating table.

So we operated on her as the sun came up over the grasslands on a clear, golden morning, and her son first breathed the rather attenuated air of the operating theatre. She was delighted, and I as pleased as if, somehow, I had had something to do with this new life on earth. We ate our breakfast, full of thanks.

The child died about three months later of a severe bout of diarrhœa. Mrs Mpanza came tearfully to tell me, explaining that it was her mother-in-law who had refused permission for her to bring the child to us, because she did not approve of the operation we had done. But another pregnancy restored her hope and she came regularly to be examined. 'Yes, I know I must come into hospital to have this second child,' she recited dutifully right up to the time when she was delivered of a dead baby at home after a long and trying labour. I was cross with her and called her a fool, which was wrong of me, but I was as pleased as she when again she became pregnant.

'This time you really will come, won't you?' I coaxed.

'Yes, doctor; I've learnt a lesson, and I shall come.'

But she stayed at home and lost the baby again under the same tragic circumstances and for the same reason; her family refused any more operations for her. She still has no children, though this all happened a number of years ago now, and moves sadly into the room when her turn comes at the clinic. 'Please, doctor, I want a baby.'

Her vacillations confirmed in us a real distaste for operative delivery in young African women for their first baby, lest they run into physical danger in subsequent home deliveries or, from fear, follow the tragic sequence of Mrs Mpanza. But you always find extroverts in all walks of life and plenty of women demand Cæsarian section at the first contraction of labour, showing not the smallest trace of anxiety.

We had held on all day watching the slow advance of Mrs Zigode's labour, until in the evening, as the sun was setting on an exhausting, strained day, we made up our minds to carry out an operative delivery. We approached her apologetically, fearful of a repetition of the other woman's infirmity of purpose. 'I'm afraid we shall have to operate on you,' we said.

She was unmoved. 'I wondered when you were going to make your minds up,' from the lofty heights of prescience, she smiled down at us and gave us her august permission.

4

In later years it has been possible, though alarmingly expensive, to obtain stored blood for transfusion, but at first any blood we gave had to be taken from a more or less willing donor, cross matched and transfused there and then into a patient whose emotional reactions to receiving blood were at the time unknown to us. We covered the early bottles with brown paper to hide the contents from the recipients, but later found this to be unnecessary as no objections were registered by patients or their relatives. The senior staff were the first donors, but to their great credit the nurses were soon volunteering their own blood when they saw that it was needed. Under the circumstances in which transfusions were given and because our laboratory facilities were only rudimentary, we had to search widely to find blood whose compatibility was beyond question. Only once the search ended at my own veins for blood to match that of a woman on whom I had been operating. Since it was from my unskilful surgery that she had lost more blood than she could afford, there was a rough justice in my being the next patient on the table, where Margaret efficiently and dispassionately ran off a pint into a bottle.

The coming of synthetic substances, which behave in some measure like human plasma in preserving the circulating blood-volume, was the beginning of a new era for country surgeons far from blood banks and laboratories. They are not cheap, but they are safe, readily available and effective. They save lives, and even at fifty shillings the bottle that is a bargain.

While patients accept blood without complaint and are undismayed by saline and glucose infusions, the ward oxygen-cylinder is an object of terror to the unsophisticated. Normally inquisitive patients saw, during their stay in the wards, too many of the elderly or severely ill slipping out of life in an atmosphere of oxygen to like the black cylinder in the little wheeled holder. They called it 'the candle' and feared its approach. Its accidental appearance beside the bed of one convalescent patient—it had been wheeled there to be out of the way while some cleaning was being done—caused her to run down the road in her nightdress; nor could we persuade her to return.

The X-ray machine was able to inspire the same terror in a few, but most patients faced X-rays, oxygen-cylinders, surgery and blood transfusions with the same air of bored indifference.

There is for me something so remarkable about X-rays that I have never lost my surprise when, as a result of pressing a switch, I am able to produce a record of the very bones of a man. Their revelation of the marvellous mechanics of our skeleton; their power to destroy living cells and in that destruction to save life itself; these wonders have never become tarnished for me.

I wanted to share my feelings with the patients and I suppose there was pride, too, in my desire to show off this almost magical invention, as if I was its originator and the guardian of its continued existence. The first time I tried, conjuror-like, to impress a patient with an X-ray picture of her chest was a dismal failure; if any one learnt anything it was myself.

'Look!' I said to the woman, 'here are your ribs, this is the heart-shadow and here, in the right lung . . .' She was not listening to my words, but sat up in bed indifferently picking her nose. I tried again. 'In the right lung, *here,*' my finger traced the lung lesion, 'in this white, fluffy area is evidence of consol . . .' But she had drifted off again, passed into another orbit. I huffily replaced the picture in its paper cover and went back to the sister's desk at the end of the ward. I was a little hurt by her indifference; surely she must understand how wonderful it all was? To be able to see your own ribs and the shadow of your heart must awaken some surprise in the untutored mind?

But my trick had fallen flat, and she had been entirely unimpressed. What had she thought of it all? Had she been articulate I think she would have expressed herself by asking in her turn what I expected out of X-ray apparatus except X-rays? It was all as far outside her experience as motor cars and refrigerators and thus had no content at all for her, either of wonder or satisfaction.

Perhaps it was not unnatural that some of the older patients, already a little scared by their entry into a new world of hospital bedsteads, of sheets and windows that opened, should feel some degree of terror at being placed under or before a piece of apparatus even as little awesome as our second-hand X-ray plant. Until they had experienced for themselves the anticlimax of that painless probing of their innermost core, many retained a caution in their approach to the couch which I reserve, from the same black ignorance, for electric plugs and wireless sets.

Margaret called Joanna Ntombela along to wait outside the X-ray room while she was still busy with the previous patient, but the old lady declined to walk along the corridor. 'Whatever is the matter now?' Margaret asked.

'I'm afraid.' Her candour was almost indecent and Margaret winced under the defiance from those skinny eyes.

'There's nothing to be afraid of, Mrs Ntombela'—Margaret's patience seldom snapped—'really, you won't feel a thing. Look, I'll walk along with you, and I promise you that you won't feel . . .'

But Joanna's 'No' was an art-form all to itself in its perfection of finality.

'Would you like to tell me what it is you are afraid of?'

'Yes, I'll tell you,' said the old lady. 'Come over here.'

Margaret went to the head of the bed. 'Now, look!' Joanna waved an arm in the direction of the corridor. 'I can see everything that's going on down there by the X-ray room.' She stopped, as if the whole thing were now explained.

'Yes?'

'I've been watching that door all afternoon.'

'Well?'

She drew up her shrunken body, exasperated by Margaret's slowness of comprehension. 'Four people have gone into that room; only three have come out!' The point was proven.

And yet she went along in the end, overcoming her fear with a courage no less real for being on a small scale.

CHAPTER ELEVEN

Magic and Mental Health

I

ON my thirty-fifth birthday the Sisters and the children of the local Roman Catholic school held a dramatic concert in my honour. For several weeks I had surprised whispered conferences between Margaret and the Sisters and more than once I fancied I had seen a white habit disappear round the corner of a building as I came along. I knew that something was up, and I knew it had to do with my birthday; I knew, too, that whatever it was sprung from a generosity of heart which I had learnt to expect from the missionary Sisters.

On the great day I was placed squarely behind a table laden with gifts—sweets and soap, handkerchiefs and pennies—with Margaret on my one hand and the priest on the other. On either side of the room was a blackboard, that on the right announcing the programme in incredibly neat copperplate script; that on the left filled with eight drawings in coloured chalks, the significance of which was at first hidden from me.

I was not to be kept long in ignorance, for a choir of small children came in from the wings and began one of those accretive songs whose choruses grow with each verse until, at the close, the whole story is sung right through. The pictures on the left hand blackboard turned out to be scenes from my life, to one of which the teacher pointed as each verse was sung.

The first showed my father, bearded, bending over my white-clad mother who held in her arms a boudoir-pink infant. This was followed by a scene from my schooldays, portrayed with illusory brilliance; a close-up of university life where someone resembling the chancellor shook me warmly by the hand; and so on until in scene eight, to the accompaniment of the full choir rehearsing my supposed virtues, I was gathered to my reward in a green glow.

It was all intensely moving for it was naïvely but wholly sincere. On my most unworthy and irascible head were heaped coals of fire that day.

Towards the bottom of the programme came a song whose approach I found I had been anticipating as each item above it was presented. The title had caught my eye, not only because it was written in large capitals, but because of its extraordinary nature; it was a single word—HYSTERIA.

The choir entered, led by the youngest, a gym-tunicked fairy, and ending with the young men of the bass in sombre maturity. Clear as a bell, and a little sharp, the sopranos opened: 'Oh! The hysteria affects us all!'

'Us all,' echoed the basses, moving into a hum.

'Oh! it gets you by the throat; it awakes you in the night!'

'In the night.'

And more than ever the boys looked mournful and bleakness sat on the girls' faces. When the song was over I was uncertain whether to clap or not. There was a brief pause, like that at the end of a concert while the audience is still wondering if there is another movement yet to come, and then a burst of excited clapping from the delighted children.

For politeness' sake I joined in the applause. Margaret lent over to me: 'Where in the world,' she whispered, 'would you find such another nice lot of children saying they were a bunch of hysterics?'

And here, indeed, was a mystery; these charming children who had saved their pennies to buy me a present, who had rehearsed and performed so polished a concert in my honour, were apparently the victims of a most hideous despair. There was no mistaking the sincerity of the song, nor the warm reception that the audience had given to it; these young people were waiting, apparently helplessly, until hysteria struck them down. And I knew only too well that some of them *would* fall victims to this trouble; so many young people did, when the stresses of first love, puberty and the conflicts between a Christian upbringing and the prevailing promiscuity of their world, fell upon them. Some of them for certain, and perhaps a great many, would one day begin to tremble and fall grunting, kicking and screaming to the ground, writhing and tearing their clothes.

This florid form of hysteria thrives in an atmosphere of excitement. It is a highly infectious condition which requires urgent isolation if it is not to spread. While there is an admiring audience there is little hope of ending an attack, but no hysteric will play to an empty house. Sharp physical stimuli, a bucket of cold water or a slap on the face, may shock the patient back to her senses, but their administration is apt to involve the therapist in the general pother, and such methods are probably best avoided altogether.

In addition to these dramatic if short-lived emotional storms, there are manifestations of hysteria more prolonged and more closely conforming to the pattern of organic disease. There are hysterical jaw pains, convulsive shaking of the shoulder blades, eye-strain, headaches and gripping sensations in the region of the heart. Sharp pains in the sides, resembling the pains of pleurisy, are particularly common and cause a great deal of confusion. Like all the many symptoms which our anxious minds project on to our tired bodies, these sharp pains are 'real' enough to the sufferer. To him they are indistinguishable from the stabbing pains of pneumonia, and he takes them every bit as seriously. At the beginning of the rains, when cold weather and swift changes of temperature produce a crop of pneumonias and the ambulance is called out daily to these gravely ill patients, there are always admitted at the same time a number of hysterics who have called the ambulance with equal urgency. It seems that no distinction is drawn between the true and the spurious pneumonia; both beg to be admitted in equal concern for their lives.

To get annoyed with a well young woman who has had the ambulance out all night for hysterical chest pains is useless, though human. If rebukes have any effect at all, they merely deter the pneumonia patients from coming to hospital, leaving the more resilient hysterics unconvicted of sin.

We learnt most of what we know about these remarkable patients from Gilmore Lee, a psychologist who spent two years with us on a research programme, investigating dreams and hysterical states among young Zulus of both sexes. He pointed out the frequency with which certain stereotyped dreams recurred, of being submerged under a flooded river, or of being pursued by little hobgoblins. To his delight, the local interpretation of these dreams was in orthodox Freudian terms, with water a birth-symbol and snakes, which kept on cropping up in the women's descriptions of their night-visions, as a sign of masculine sexuality. A snake dream cost one woman the index finger of her right hand. 'I dreamt,' she said as she unwrapped the almost severed end of the finger, 'that I caught one of the snakes and bit its head off.'

For many their dreams are in every respect as real as the waking world about them. 'Have you ever seen the Water-Sprite?' I asked a woman who persisted that he was the cause of all her symptoms. 'Oh, yes; I often see him when I'm asleep,' she replied.

When a patient's catalogue of symptoms seems to make even less sense than usual and he and the doctor seem hopelessly at cross purposes, an inquiry about recent dreams may clarify things wonderfully. There dawns a feeling that, at last, the doctor is getting down to what really matters, and cheerfulness enters the consultation where before there was only mounting mutual irritation. Yet patiently to hear the tales of harrowing dreams and nightly visitations is one thing, and to do anything useful about them is quite another, especially where points of view are so radically at variance.

We have become accustomed to the idea that our dreams and anxieties arise from within ourselves; we realize well enough that the rejected thought of the daylight hours may rise again at night to work itself out while the censor of our mind sleeps. In medieval times we should have looked outside ourselves for the origin of these visions, just as to-day the Zulu Diviner will interpret his dreams as being sent from such and such an ancestor. Looked at their way, dreams are warnings, messages and reproofs from the spirit world; they are real, important and may be denied only at a man's peril.

2

The very call which makes a young man or woman take up the profession of Diviner comes through a dream. The postulant is granted a vision of the great python which lies curled at the bottom of a mystic river, and knows that this is a call to take up the ancient cult of his ancestors. The visitation may be rejected at first, for often the postulant has no conscious wish to become a Diviner, but the dream will be repeated with increasing frequency until he knows that to delay further means sickness or even death. Indeed in some sense he is ill already; there are strange churning movements in the abdomen, sharp pains in the chest and a heaviness over the shoulders as if Someone was pressing him forward. His behaviour alters, he becomes withdrawn, shunning the company of others, afflicted by heavy sighs, paroxysms of sneezing and sonorous eructations. One day he will walk away from his home, saying nothing to his family, and pass in a dream-like trance through country unknown to him until, as if by fate, he meets with a Diviner who is already well along the path the neophyte must tread. From the Diviner he learns his art and during his novitiate he adopts the dress and manner of his new profession. He raddles his face with ochre and adopts women's dress. Crossed over his chest he wears a sort of Sam Browne of goat skin, and in his hair are the gall bladders of sacrificial goats.

The force of this mysterious call is such that it takes precedence over family considerations or religious loyalties. Janet Zungu was a decent Christian woman, a communicant and a regular church-goer, until she was admitted to hospital complaining of pains in her chest and shoulders. Careful examination revealed no organic cause for these symptoms and the X-ray picture showed nothing untoward in the lung-fields. I referred her to Gilmore Lee; could he please find anything to account for this woman's illness? The two of them got on wonderfully well together; a lot of useful information came out of their talks, and in the end Mrs Zungu suddenly declared herself perfectly well again and anxious to return to her home. For six months afterwards we lost touch with her and when she reappeared she was transformed; she was fat and well, and dressed in the uniform of a Diviner. Of Lee she could not say enough; that it was he who had put her on the right path, and that he understood her people in a way that very few white men have ever understood them. On his unwilling shoulders she laid the whole responsibility for her present condition and her heart was full of thanks. It was all deeply embarrassing for Lee and for ourselves; broad as was our mandate from the Missionary Society, I was uneasily aware that it did not extend to the selection and training of Diviners.

Now, when I see her about the hospital, I ask her whether she plans to return to the Church? 'No,' she smiles, 'no, not yet.'

Resolution of these emotional states in even the qualifiedly successful manner of Mrs Zungu is often incomplete, and while the screaming hysteria of young girls can be expected to pass with time, the physical disorders which stem from anxiety are less hopeful of cure. Young men convinced they are harbouring snakes in their abdomens present a formidable challenge to their doctors.

To those prepared to believe, the normal rumblings of intestinal gas and the customary churnings of the bowel about its daily work are considered to be evidence of a snake moving about inside, feeding upon the body of the unfortunate host. Perhaps it is not so surprising that the sounds issuing with such embarrassing clarity from the bowels of the faithful at Holy Communion should be attributed to such origins, but the results of this mystical parasitism are disastrous. The patient suffers constant, gnawing pain, he loses weight and appetite and falls a melancholy victim to sad-faced introspection by day and snake-infested dreams by night.

Looking back on these cases we have seen that in some instances they were in the early stages of recognizable mental disorder. I do not think we have materially helped any of them, nor, since some of them come to us at second hand from the medicine-man and the Diviner, am I prepared to grant to these indigenous practitioners a very much greater measure of success. It is fashionable to believe that medicine-men are gifted with extraordinary powers for dealing with this type of case, but the evidence is, alas, to the contrary. It is small comfort to share in failure, but for once the doctor and the indigenous therapist seem to be equally impotent.

Mrs Masuku came to me with her chest wall already marked with the close parallel scars which are the sign of the medicine-man's attentions. She had a pain in her chest just under the site of the scarification whence, she claimed, a piece of baboon skin had been drawn by cupping. 'It was this big,' she indicated a square of about three inches side, 'and all hairy.'

'But you've still got your pain,' I pointed out.

'Yes, that's true; I've still got the pain.'

I undertook to try to rid her of this discomfort, but made no promises that my treatment would produce anything half so satisfying as a piece of baboon-skin. We X-rayed her and did all we knew, but for her pain we could find no cause, nor was she one whit better when she left us than she had been when she had tired of her sorcerer.

For what the patient ascribes to magical causes it is often possible to find an origin in more prosaic physical disorder. The physician is never absolved—no matter how neatly the psychological peg fits in the diagnostic hole—from a sober, detailed assessment of his patient. Over Sithomo's son I havered just long enough to turn the scales against him because I forgot this lesson. Had I pressed home my investigations with vigour and completed them in one or two days instead of two or three weeks, I might have been able to persuade his father to permit the operation which would in all probability have saved his life. He was a mournful young man, withdrawn and hypochondriac. His complaint was of abdominal pain, repeated vomiting and loss of weight, and physical examination was entirely negative. He and his family considered his troubles were the result of a snake in his belly and I was inclined to go more than half-way to meet them, putting everything down to psychological causes. By the time the diagnosis was established, confidence had waned; the boy's father, sensing our uncertainty, refused the operation we advised and took him home, where, in a week or two, he died.

There are plenty of tales of cures affected by cunning in these cases. The usual story is that the patient is given an anæsthetic, his skin incised and sutured again, and a dead snake shown to him the following day as the one removed from his abdomen. Like the relation of ghostly experiences the stories are invariably at second hand and, apart from the stink

13. *A nurses' tutorial*

14. *Young patients keep up with the news*

of quackery which rises about their telling, it seems unlikely that the treatment would be of any use; we are, after all, trying to remove the torment from a sufferer's mind and not a snake from his alimentary canal.

Physical relief may be insufficient to save the patient where the mental component of his illness remains unresolved. Convinced she was harbouring a snake, one woman had seen a surgeon in Johannesburg. What organic disorder he had found at operation, or what he had been able to do for her relief I do not know, for she came to us dying and without her notes. But whatever the surgeon had been able to do, her symptoms must have persisted. 'You see,' she whispered shortly before she died, 'he did his best for me, but he never found the snake.'

3

The mentally disordered go almost entirely unrelieved. Throughout the Province of Natal there are only two institutions struggling against over-crowding and staff shortage to help the mentally ill. All that can be done is done, but most of those who might benefit by treatment have no hope at all of obtaining it. Paradoxically the best chance of securing a place for these patients is for them to lift violent hands against their neighbours; then, through the processes of the law, they may find themselves com-mitted to the Mental Hospital. For the withdrawn, the quiet and the agreeable feeble-minded there is no hope at all, their care falling upon their distracted relatives.

Nothing about the ordinary Zulu home is suitable for the management of a mental patient. There are seldom any able bodied men who are not away at work; the houses are inflammable; hosts of children play about the compound all day long. Even if the patient is quiet there is still the problem of his support, the provision of his food and clothing; if he is violent and aggressive the other members of the family go daily in danger of their lives. Arson, assault and murder can and do happen under these circumstances and the family takes the only precaution it can, binding the sufferer with leather thongs. Ragged and fifthy, under-fed and unwanted, these unfortunates sit day by day in the sun, hopeless and unrelieved as the thongs wear into their skin and misery marks their faces.

Nor could we do much to help; mental patients respond poorly in the general wards where in any case their presence causes such disturbance that we are reluctant to admit them. Only in those mental breakdowns resulting from malnutrition—the cases of pellagra—is there sure enough hope of cure in a reasonable length of time, and these we take in, treat.

and have the pleasure of watching their restoration. We can manage, too, a few of the elderly whose minds have become confused in time and place and whose memories are waning with the slow diminution of their cerebral blood-supply.

But towards the violent, and the young psychotics we have had to harden our hearts and return them to their own people and to the whole wretched routine of bonds and hunger which is theirs at home.

For the comparatively few who are violent or incapable, there are many whose infirmity hardly qualifies for madness, among whom are the eccentric, the constitutionally over-cheerful and the simple-minded. Many are regular visitors to the hospital, some for its free meals—gleaned from the cooking pots and the waste-bins—others for the unrivalled opportunities the hospital affords for deviational religious behaviour.

Ophelia—so we call her, not knowing her name—binds garlands on her ochred brow of the brightest blooms from our herbaceous borders. Taking from her flower-crowned head a non-existent biretta, she hands it to her ghostly chaplain and genuflects with supreme dignity to the water-butts or—more embarrassingly, but fortunately less often—to the doctor on duty. We should be the poorer without her visits, just as we should miss old Josias who claims at 75 to be afflicted with the crying hysteria of young girls. He comes sometimes in the evenings as we are locking up the out-patient building for the night. When he does it is useless to argue; better to get the keys out again and unlock the dispensary. He drinks the bottle he gets in one long, splendid draught, so that for him alone, knowing his habits, we are sometimes guilty of watering his medicine.

4

To a certain extent, belief in magic and the influence of the Little People was a comforting philosophy. It absolved the believer from responsibility for his acts, since everything that happened, happened from causes beyond himself. The milk went sour, not because the milk buckets were dirty, but from the spite of goblins.

But the Little People are shy and cannot bear the new ways of the world; everywhere they are quitting their heritage before the advancing fronts of industrialization and education. And a man deserted by them, seeing for the first time how much depends upon himself, may be forgiven a sense of bewilderment and even resentment.

Upon the schoolchild in the upper forms the realization of his essential loneliness may burst with sufficient suddenness to cause a temporary emotional breakdown. The logic which has brought him to this moment of awareness precludes his screaming his tensions away in hysteria as his simpler brothers and sisters might do; instead he may become moody and difficult, sunk in self-pity, or fall a prey to headaches and 'eye strain.' The wonder of the whole phase is not that these children should show a morbid interest in hysteria like my entertainers at the school concert, but that so many should weather the storm and, facing their problems, solve them. For many do become worthwhile nurses, teachers and leaders of the next generation for whom, perhaps, the fight will be a little less lonely, a little easier.

But far more are never brought face to face with their spiritual solitude. For them the world is still peopled with a third order of bogles and sprites. In the strange, erotic dreams which the Diviners, anticipating Freud by centuries, so accurately interpreted; in the transmitted visions of the fey, the Little People live on. Children to whom for the most part he is friendly, can see the Water-Sprite. At puberty he passes not alone from vision but from memory also, thereafter persisting only as a visitor in the world of dreams, menacing and ithyphallic. Alpheus could see him still, even though he was an adult, but then Alpheus was mad. I would ask him if the Sprite was about? And he, creasing a forehead already autographed by misery, would stare intently in front of him. 'There he is!' he would point to a corner of the room. 'He is sitting looking at you. There—*There*—' He would grasp my arm in his urgency—but I could never see the Sprite.

With so many unseen and malignant influences abroad it is small wonder that fear of their dreadful visitations is a constant preoccupation with the mothers of small children. Even so, before the days of universal inoculation against diphtheria, must English mothers have listened fearfully for the first croupy spasms in their baby's throat which would herald the cruel robbery of infant death.

Healthy infants are brought to the doctor because they cry a lot; or wake with a start in the night; or sigh; or show unexplained fear in the presence of strangers. Apart from those in whom some cause can be found for these indefinite symptoms—an inflamed ear or a blocked nose—there remain many for whom physical examination reveals nothing. Indeed from their smiling faces and toothless grins it is evident that all is well with the children, yet the mothers are worried to the point of panic. The question, which is never asked directly but always by implication, is whether this child will die as suddenly and unexpectedly as the two previous children? They were just as fat and bonny as this one, yet one morning they were found cold and dead in their blankets. 'They were not ill; they just died,' say the mothers.

What by the women is attributed to witchcraft has usually a simpler more workaday explanation. Many of the children die of diarrhœa which—surprisingly in view of its high toll of infant life—is not considered serious, taking second place to that harmless old bogy of the nursery, constipation. But diarrhœa, or pneumonia or meningitis, can carry off a child in a few hours, and it is the speed and suddenness of the death which gives to these tragedies a mysterious quality, at any rate in the eyes of those who are looking for mystery.

On the data the mothers possess, knowing nothing of infections, it is understandable that they have concluded that their children carry within them a tendency to spontaneous and sudden death. They have, by repeated bereavement, come to think of the sleek, healthy appearance of their babies as a cruel deception; that each child carries within itself a kind of Original Illness with which it was born and to which, if it is not properly protected, it will succumb.

Of this Original Illness the child must be cleansed, and where else should the cleansing begin but in the bowel? The idea that the bowel contents are poisonous is as old as mankind and as universal as funerals. Cleaning out the bowel was a medical preoccupation from the dawn of time until its fine flowering under the nineteenth century physicians; respectable textbooks to this day carry an injunction to give an aperient at the beginning of almost every disorder known to science; the Zulu mothers know that to get rid of the 'filth' inside their babies is the first step in the complicated business of their protection against the baleful consequences of Original Illness.

The infant bowel is washed by the giving of an enema of soap and water introduced from the mother's mouth through a hollow reed. This is the first and most important of a sequence of enemas administered up to three times daily throughout the first year of a baby's life. 'He doesn't get his bowels open unless I do,' say the mothers when asked the reason for this enthusiasm; from the frequency and thoroughness of the process it is not surprising that the tortured bowel has little energy left for spontaneous evacuation.

In addition to the giving of enemas, there are other steps which may be taken by the medicine-men for the protection of the child. The most important is the symbolic burying of the child at a point in the ground where lightning has at some time struck. There a hole is dug and the child induced, by yet another enema, to relieve itself into the hole. The soil is replaced and the child taken away from the scene, no one being permitted to look backwards at the scene of the burial. Scarification and the inunction of protective medicines into the little cuts should be done at the same time, paying particular attention to the umbilical region and the outer surfaces of the joints.

By properly observing the precautions and, thereafter, by the wearing of amulets containing medicine, it seems possible to confer upon children a degree of immunity from the evil influences that everywhere abound. Certainly, few children are passed over in this cleansing process. Even among sophisticated people, where formal belief in the efficacy of these measures has long since died away, they are still done to be on the safe side, though not without a few blushes and shy apologies to the doctor.

By the same token, our own preoccupation with preventive injections against diphtheria and poliomyelitis is taken as eminently reasonable and meets with ready co-operation. To labour any slight difference there might be between controlled inoculation and ritual scarification does not produce results commensurate with the effort of explanation. It is better to let old custom help you where it can than to indulge in criticism, however right your point of view.

CHAPTER TWELVE

The Wheel Reconsidered

I

OLD Sea-Water was the last son of Cetshwayo, the Zulu king who had, for a few weeks in the summer of 1879, maintained an army in the field against the might of Chelmsford's Imperial troops. He was immensely fat, waxed his moustaches and wore a semi-military uniform of his own devising which gave him an air of authority. But fat is the enemy of long life and, in the end, fat took its toll. His heart wearied of its 300lb. burden and failed, swelling his already gross body with dropsy and causing him to pant at the slightest exertion.

He sent his request to come into the hospital through the Magistrate as it was perfectly proper for him to do, and the Magistrate passed the message on to me. In deference to his royal origin I drove the ambulance myself. It was a rough journey even by Zululand standards, the last stages of the climb up the hill to his home being over bare sandstone, bedded in layers more like a staircase than a road, over which the truck boiled and lurched in protest. By the house were the bones of another vehicle which had once tried the ascent in former times, and so died. It had been a Buick, with a collapsible hood for the protection of the passengers from the sun's heat or the sharp needles of summer rain; now it lay, nose down in a bed of thorn-apples, its buff paint a prey to the cancerous advance of rust, its tyres long gone to sole the sandals of sons and strangers, its hood and upholstery ripped by the hands of men and consumed by the busy jaws of white ants. A gauge on the dashboard registered as full the petrol tank that lay a few yards away.

Nowadays there is a brisk market in second-hand motor vehicles which bounce recklessly over the roads of the Reserves on their passage to the scrapheap, but when this Buick made its first and last ascent to the hill-top it was a pioneer, representing much of human hope and glory. Even so, I doubt if its swift death and protracted decay caused many heartaches; its hour had been and was gone; while it lasted it had been very good.

I announced my arrival outside the chief's room and was told to go in.

He was propped up in a huge brass-balled bedstead of the late, decadent period of iron bedstead design, whence he greeted me breathlessly but kindly. I asked him a few questions to which he wheezed the answers through plum-coloured lips; his feet, he told me, were swollen to twice their proper size. Certainly there seemed little connection between the neat boots by the bedside and the pachydermic feet that had once been able to wear them.

Climbing on to the bed—for I could not reach him from the side where he lay—I examined him and listened to the tumultuous running of his old heart, halting, stumbling, galloping again, failing in its efforts to keep the blood circulating through the uttermost capillaries of that great frame. He was gravely ill, and knew it, and was willing enough to risk the journey down the hill-side to the hospital. With his permission I waited outside to photograph him as he came out of his house, but it was not he who emerged first from the door, but a gnome whose large head, decorated by the pits of smallpox, contrasted with the small body which bore it. In his hands the gnome carried an enamel chamber-pot, scarred by night-time collisions with the bed legs, yet still borne ceremoniously as men carried the gourds which served the same office to the great ones of olden times. The Chief followed, supported by two headmen, and stood panting in the doorway while I took my picture; after which his helpers prized him into the front seat while I climbed into the narrow space that remained under the shelter of the steering wheel.

The old man was inclined at first to be talkative and told me about his father whom he said he remembered well. Crossing the plain below the mountain we fell silent until he saw a schoolgirl coming along the track towards us. 'You see that girl?' he asked.

I nodded.

'Run her over for me.' It was a command.

'I can't do that, Chief,' I remonstrated, 'we should kill her.'

He sniffed at my softness. 'My father would have run her over,' he pronounced as we passed the girl. She, unaware of her peril, went on kicking a pebble carelessly along the track and never looked up to salute the son of her great king.

Though there lingered in his dying body something of the old barbarian, he was an exemplary patient and I only wish I had known in return how to behave to so historic a character. My attempts to behave appropriately were unconvincing, but he was magnanimous and forgiving towards a foreigner's ignorance of ceremony. He carried out our requests with a dignity not untouched by humour.

We permitted his henchmen to lie on the floor of his private ward at night and to be present whenever he wished them to be in the daytime. Eventually he died and his friends made him a crude coffin into which, somehow, we managed to lift him.

With him passed an era; his superb self-confidence and magnificent assurance were no doubt but barbaric virtues, but in a world of half-held creeds and timidity which passes for humility, they shone brightly enough.

2

For such as he, too ill to reach medical help, the ambulance service was planned and by the mortally ill it is used with increasing frequency. It is also used by the lazy; the slow-of-thought who remember on Friday morning that Thursday was clinic day; and by the frightened, whose panic grows with the advancing darkness of evening. The service suffers from the defect that the patient, or his family, are the only possible arbiters of whether the ambulance should be called; and their decision owes less as a rule to logic than to the emotions.

Thus it is that we often make fruitless journeys over cattle tracks or through the moonscape of dessicated water-courses to find at our destination a woman with a needle in her hand or the complainant in an assault case more injured in his pride than in his person. There is no way of telling; the message comes to us by telephone from a neighbouring store, more often than not handed in by the fool of the family who himself does not know what is wrong with the patient. It might be a grave injury, it might be a minor sore throat; it might be a woman or it might be a man; seldom indeed can the likely diagnosis be made from any information obtained from the telephone message. You grumble, but you go, and there are many surprises, quite apart from the inevitable proportion of maternity cases in which your arrival is anticipated by the baby's. Hauled out of bed one night I journeyed fifteen miles to arrive at a home just in time to be barged out of the way by four exultant women who emerged through the hut door as I was about to enter. They took no notice of me whatever as they encircled the hut, crying out in their delight and beating the thatch with their hands as they went. 'Excuse me'—I tried to make my presence felt in the darkness—'Here, I say . . .' but the women went on beating and ignored me completely. Finally one of them broke away. 'Good evening, doctor,' she said, as if nothing unusual was going on. 'She's had the baby.' I growled something about that being pretty obvious and climbed into the driving cab.

'Aren't you coming in to see the baby?' they invited.

'No, I'm not,' I answered surlily. Then I repented and went to see the pink cause of all this delight. The mother, who had attended ante-natal clinic the week before, looked so supremely complacent that my ill humour melted a little. I looked dutifully at the baby, which was clearly expected of me, said good night and received in return an effusion of thanks I had ill deserved, and then retired.

Overhead, Orion hung head downwards in the sky and the milky way winked in the soft night, a million million points of light to restore a sense of proportion.

3

For months on end the clean sun, which in these latitudes is never up vulgarly early, even in midsummer, tops the last eastern ridge and shines fiercely and impartially through hut doors and boudoir windows without the lightest cloud to muffle his insistence. In the same bright months he dessicates the grasslands in his twelve-hour passage and sinks, an antiseptic coughdrop, below the western hills. Picnics and garden fêtes could be arranged without precautionary preparation of the parish hall were this the country of garden parties and were there any parish halls. As it is, the bright months are the months of the emergence of inspectors on inspection, health visitors, evangelists, tourists, film companies, sociologists and, though rarer, hunters to destroy in the name of sport and for the sake of their stringy flesh, the small but irreplaceable vermin of the grasslands, the splendid game birds and the bouncing buck.

The traveller at this time has good expectation of reaching his destination; only the taste of the road's dust between his teeth and a soiled collar will give him any inconvenience.

After the bright months come the wet ones; the months of summer when the weary, unchanging blue of the sky becomes a built-up area of cloud castles; when deceptive dawns give place to shrouded, angry afternoons of hail and tempest; when the grass turns green again and the dry earth puts on its floral cretonnes; when red dust turns to tomato soup and it is no longer certain where the traveller will end his journey. He is more likely to spend his nights in bed who takes with him chains for the wheels, a tow-rope, a spade and a couple of sacks. The penalty for being among the foolish virgins is here, as elsewhere, stern and unbending.

With the coming of the hot, wet weather and its attendant host of houseflies, diarrhœa and typhoid become more prevalent. For these diseases, added as they are to the steady incidence of non-seasonal sickness, the ambulance is called frequently and without much thought being wasted upon driver or vehicle. The only limiting factor is the ability of the messenger to make contact with the hospital, and this, by telephone or foot, can usually be accomplished.

It was still a brilliant morning when they called the ambulance to fetch Mseleku's second wife, and for some reason or other I drove the thirty-five mile journey myself. The outward journey was easy, with the sun shining warmly in spite of low, dark clouds already forming in the west where lay, invisible in the haze, the high ridges and terraced peaks of the Drakensberg mountains. From the last river to the hill top where Mseleku has his home is just five miles, but it is five miles of rutted track, steep rises, jutting rocks and narrow causeways over boggy reed-green springs where arum lilies bloom in summer, white bride-flowers, groomless and unprized.

By the time I reached the home the vast grey fan of cloud had extended up the sky with quite unusual speed. It was dramatic, but I did not concern myself much over its rising; it never rains in the mornings I told myself.

The home was in the old style, as men built their houses before the first paraffin tins were hammered into roofing tiles, or corrugated iron had found its way into the remotest corners of the district. Each hut was a dome of thin branches made supple by soaking in the river, then bent over and lashed together with bark strips. Over the framework was thick thatch tied down with a mesh of grass rope. There was no window and no chimney and the doorway was an arch no more than two feet six inches high. Through this low entrance I crept on hands and knees, preserving what I could under the circumstances of a doctor's dignity. Inside, the darkness was velvet, impenetrable to eyes dazzled by the sunshine in the compound, but I could hear the patient's breathing from the other side of the hut; the grunting, anxious respirations of pneumonia.

The light-blindness passed and in the cool gloom of that interior I could make out the shrouded figures of women, propped like sacks around the wall. There were more of them than the hut could possibly hold— or so it seemed—silently sitting, watching through the dragging hours. It was impossible to guess what held them there, congealed in that shadowy wake; curiosity, fear, complacency, love? These certainly, and who knows what mixtures of other emotions?

I squatted in silence for three or four minutes, self-consciously well mannered, waiting until I was spoken to, determined not to be the first to break that silence. From somewhere at the back of the hut a woman greeted me as if she had just recognized my presence. We exchanged the courtesies and lapsed again into silence. For a while longer I waited for some lead, some invitation to examine the sick woman, but none came. My nerve cracked. 'Well, now,' I said, a little too loudly, 'is this the patient?' I crossed the floor and started to be business-like and white.

She was ill; her one lung solid with pneumonia. Through the chest wall I could hear the harsh passage of her breath transmitted by the sodden lung; her burning skin radiated heat like an electric fire, her lips were parched, cracked and littered with dry spittle and flakes of desquamated skin. 'She's ill,' I pronounced, and the waiting women echoed my words : 'Yes, she is ill; ill indeed.'

It would be a long journey back for her and a desperately bumpy one, but her life depended on her making it. A hopefully large dose of penicillin, or a little mound of sulphonamide tablets beside her sleeping mat would not answer; she was in need of nursing; in need of fluids to replace the water her body was losing by her swift breathing and from her hot skin. Somehow or other we had got to get Mrs Mseleku down the mountain.

A sudden gust of wind tugging at the thatch made me look out through the doorway. The arc of storm cloud was already past the zenith and still moving fast towards the east, its elephantine belly underslung with whitish polyps of cloud. Here and there in its substance shone a glint of ice-green, betokening hail.

The first drops of rain whacked down on the yard, drawing a chill, electric scent from the damped earth. Then silence; an absolute stillness that the wind obeyed, dropping to nothing; a silence of birds and humans; a silence padding the space between the herald-drops of rain and the full force of the storm. Down the valley a curtain was lowered from the cloud, obscuring the fields and the little houses. There was a faint sound, a rustle of silk, to mark its falling; a sound which swelled to a drum roll as the curtain of hail swept towards us. Smacking off the rocks and bounding from the grass the first hail-stones—ice balls two inches across—fell, and with their falling, a screaming maniac wind was released from under the cloud. It bent the wild peach trees almost to the earth and sent a tin basin bowling past the doorway where we sat; under its whip the maize stalks were cut to ribbons by the flying hail and their leaves ripped away into the grey fury of the storm. Between the shafts of falling hail ran lightning, feeling for the weak spots in the earth with fingers of violet fire. So close was its touch that the thunder followed it in a single shock of sound and light.

In less than half an hour the storm had passed, leaving three inches of water and melting ice to run off the mutilated fields. As we stepped out into the watery sunlight we could see the muddy cataracts forming in the folds of the hills, like torrents of spilt gravy on a green plush table-cloth.

We cushioned the back of the truck with straw and laid the woman on a goat-skin, her head couched on the broad thighs of her mother-in-law. The road was not too bad, most of the water having drained away before it had had time to soak in, so that we made fair progress until we came to the river. There, the morning's innocent, sunsplashed waters were changed into a brutish, coffee-coloured flood. A mile downstream rose a plume of spray high over the place where the whole body of water crashed two hundred feet into a narrow scrub-choked ravine. The air was sticky, smelling of damp sports coats and wet hair.

In gum-boots and a smart city-mackintosh, the wife of the trader who kept the store on the opposite bank, came down to the river.

'What are my chances?' I shouted.

She turned both her thumbs down forcibly. 'You'll have to wait until it drops a bit'—I could just hear her answer above the din.

She was obviously right. I sat down to wait. Flood waters in these hill streams fall quickly enough as a rule.

I went round to the back to tell the mother-in-law. 'How is she now?' I asked.

'She says her breathing hurts her.'

I looked again at the woman who was wide-eyed and alertly watchful. We could afford to wait, provided the waiting was not too long.

Hynotized by the noise and the undulations of the storm-water, I began after an hour to persuade myself that the level of the river was falling. It was so essential that it should fall; the woman was not going to last for ever in the back there. Soon it would be cold when the sun went below the hills. I decided we had waited long enough.

With the engine racing we made unexpectedly good progress right up to the point where the front wheels plunged into the sandbank. This had certainly not been there in the morning, and the same brown waters that had built it, hid it also. We stopped, and the engine failed. Very gently the back of the vehicle began to move downstream towards the waterfall. But the sand, which held us prisoner in front, stopped this movement also and we came to rest with the rear well down in the water. Looking through the back window I could see that the patient's feet were just clear of the little waves that lapped the floorboards.

Contrite, I waded ashore where I was met by the trader. He made no comment on my folly. 'We'll have to get oxen to pull you out of *that*,' he said. He would have helped us in any case, but our troubles gave him a chance to try out a new span of six oxen he had recently bought. He yoked them proudly, attaching them by a long chain to the front bumper. 'Now!' he shouted, and the drover cracked his whip and the leader pulled. Nothing happened at all. 'Again!' he commanded, but the oxen only yawed over the bank in fruitless inco-ordination. Someone brought six more beasts which were yoked with the first team, but we remained hopelessly stuck.

Someone from among the crowd of spectators suggested 'lifting her out,' which seemed the most unhelpful thought that had occurred to any one yet, but I was getting worried and agreed it was worth a try. Ten men stood round the back of the truck, bending to grasp the bumper and take hold of the mudguards. A cantor sang a bar of a shanty, which was echoed by the others. Again the shanty-man; again the answer. Suddenly the back began to move. The ten men splashed round to the front; once more the verse and the gruff chorus; the front moved.

So we went, crab-wise over the sandbank until it was possible to push the last few feet up the bank. The engine started as I let in the clutch and I waved my thanks to the pushers. The trader was standing by himself, looking sadly at his new oxen. I could see his lips working as I pulled away and though I could imagine what he was saying to those six creatures, I was unable to hear exactly how he phrased it.

4

It often happens that it is impossible to reach the home by ambulance and the last part of the journey has to be completed on foot or, less often and more miserably for me, on horseback. One Good Friday my progress had been barred by a deep gully around which I could find no way for the car to pass. I was alone, and set off for the patient's home carrying a stretcher on my shoulder. The afternoon was hot and dry and the track wound endlessly between the fields of drying maize. Eventually a woman, walking fast, caught up with me from behind. She passed me, talking as she went.

'Who are you?'

'Barker.'

'Where have you come from?'

'The hospital.'

'Where is your car?' All Europeans have cars.

'I left it at the gully.'

'Where are you going?'

'I'm going to Manyathi's place to fetch his daughter.'

She was pulling ahead now and her words came less distinctly. 'What is that thing you are carrying on your shoulders?'

'It is a stretcher.'

She was silent and I thought she had finished her catechism, but she turned again and shouted back, 'Is it heavy?'

'Yes, ma, it's damned heavy,' I shouted back, but she was out of earshot or affected to be so. I plodded on carrying the stretcher which grew no lighter as the miles went by.

Manyathi's daughter was ill, all right, and the effort to reach her had not been wasted. But there seemed to be only one toothless old woman with her and no menfolk at all to help get her back as far as the ambulance.

'How are we going to get her to the hospital?' I asked.

'I don't know,' said the old woman.

'Where are the men?'

'I don't know.' She took snuff, looking bored.

'Have you any cattle?'

'No.'

I decided to explore for myself, find cattle and harness them to some sort of conveyance, even if I had to steal it. Near the cooking hut was a useable sledge which would do very well. It was a V of wood, with cross-slats attached and a chain passed through a hole in the apex of the V. Ox-drawn, these sledges are used for taking the plough to and from the fields in the spring and for bringing home the harvest in the autumn. Granted a few oxen we could manage well enough. Extending my search I came unexpectedly upon Manyathi's eldest son sitting with his back to the cattle enclosure and dozing in lofty indifference to his sister's sufferings.

'What do you think you're doing here?' I shouted at him. 'Don't you know I've come to get your sister?'

He stared back at me rudely. 'Yes, I know. I sent for you.'

'Then what the devil are you doing sitting here like a slug in the sun?' I was jabbering in English at him, forgetting a golden rule to rebuke always in the other man's language lest you say something of which you may later be ashamed. 'Get up and yoke your oxen, and hurry up, please.'

'I haven't got any oxen.'

I looked over the wall into the cattle enclosure; it was littered with the recent droppings of a sizeable herd. 'I suppose you did all that yourself, then?' I asked, but his English was not up to it.

He understood clearly enough what I wanted and, manners having reasserted themselves, I went back into Zulu, pointing out gently that there were in fact a number of oxen he could use.

'They're not mine,' he said complacently.

'Whose are they, then?'

'My brother's.'

I sighed. 'And where is your brother?'

'He's in Johannesburg—too far.'

'Can't we use them to take your sister as far as the ambulance?'

'No, that could not be done unless we ask him.'

My hackles were rising again and I countered with asperity : 'All right, we shall have to carry her on the stretcher, that's all,' and I went to pick up the stretcher from where it lay by the hut door.

'Just a minute.' Manyathi was thinking over his position. He dived into another hut, pulled out a boy of six from somewhere inside and sent him racing over the fields to where a dozen cattle were grazing in the mixed company of goats and donkeys. 'The boy has gone to get oxen,' he said civilly and in English.

We yoked them when they came, both of us extravagantly well mannered towards each other. 'If the doctor would kindly . . .?' 'Not at all. Is this right?'

Placing skins on the floorboards we placed the woman on the sledge. The small boy took the lead, Manyathi cracked his whip and the procession moved off.

No one knows who invented the wheel, any more than we know who first drew the gentle sweep of axe handles or the subtle, rustic curve of the scythe. Certainly, until modern times there have been no wheels in Zululand, and that which could not be carried on the heads of the womenfolk was transported by these simple sledges. They are not uncomfortable for they side-slip when they come to a boulder, rather than bounce over it, so that their progress, slow and sinuous as it is, is none-the-less unexpectedly smooth.

The oxen were tired by the time we reached the ambulance; they stood waiting, drawing great gulps of the cool evening air into the ribbed darkness of their deep chests while we put the patient into the cab for her greater comfort. The sky was still bright enough in the west to make the headlamps useless, yet too dark for me to see really well where we were going. Thus I did not see the cross-drain in the road before I came upon it, going a little too fast. The impact lifted us both clear of the seat and up to the cab roof; the engine stopped. We sat for a moment, collecting ourselves after the biggest jolt of the entire journey. I remember wondering whether the invention of the wheel was quite such a victory for civilization, after all?

CHAPTER THIRTEEN

District Surgeon

I

FOR rather less than £1 a day—mileage allowance extra, private practice permitted, provide for yourself an efficient mode of transport—I was retained as district surgeon, a position of protean responsibilities and negligible social importance. My duties included the certification of lunatics; the care of the indigent; inspection of the gaol and attendance at corporal punishment; the control of epidemics; the follow-up of cases of Hansen's disease; the treatment of venereal disorders and such professional services as might be possible in cases of battle, murder and sudden death.

Police officers are also eligible for free treatment from the district surgeon and, in the case of Europeans, this privilege extends to members of their families. Oddly, the dependants of African policemen are supposed to pay for their medical attention, perhaps because the limits of the constables' families are so diffuse; almost everybody can trace a relationship of some sort with one or other of the constables. Whatever the reason, it seemed unjust that these men, whose wages are so much lower than those of the Europeans, should have to pay for their families' illness, so I accepted voluntarily in my capacity as mission doctor the care I could not offer as a part-time Government employee.

Every week I had to visit the jail. This stone fortress, standing in the centre of the village, is a relic of a sterner era in the relationships between white men and black in Zululand, and still has, along its façade, loopholes for riflemen. Its high surrounding wall is crowned with jagged broken bottles, brown and green and white, relics themselves of rackety horsedrawn days when gold was mined in the district and prospectors came into the village to wash the dust from their throats. The old bar of wood and iron where they drank has been pulled down and a decent single-storey hotel stands in its place; only the frieze of shattered glass along the gaol-house wall remains to recall their heroic, legendary parties.

At the jail the District Surgeon is treated like a prince. From a succession of jailers of impeccable manners and even from the well-drilled prisoners themselves, I have received such military deference as could not fail to flatter. Entrance is gained by beating a baroque knocker against a huge steel door. There is a shuffle, a cry, a jangling of keys and the peep-hole by the knocker is slid open to reveal a gleaming warder's eye. The door swings open, and before you can cross the threshold, the warder is locked in rigid salute. There follows a courteous invitation to peer in the cooking pots, to taste the beans for to-night's supper; a brief glance in the cells where everything is in an agony of tidiness, then back to the gaoler's office to sign the books. Under each heading in the inspector's book I dutifully write 'In good condition.' Looking at its first pages, which date back twenty-odd years and three District Surgeons ago, I see that no one has ever dared to write anything else in that copy-book.

Apart from the complex of the jail, the courthouse and the offices of the Native Commissioner, there are no public buildings in the village. Certainly there is no school, and the War Memorial Hall and the hospital exist solely as the result of voluntary effort. But as the gaol is, after the hospital, the most frequented building in the district, perhaps its place in the centre of the village is not so greatly undeserved.

While there is a regular supply of prisoners, there are very few crimi-nals. Most of the inmates of the jail are defaulters from the payment of poll-tax, the drunk and disorderly and those convicted of brawling. Stock theft leads to some of the longest sentences, but it must be an exhilarating crime to commit, for many who have served one sentence for stealing their neighbours' cattle, return again for second and even third terms of imprisonment for the same crime. From among these recidivists the cooks and trusties are recruited, and many achieve a sort of eminence in that captive community which seems to make them reasonably content, even with prison life.

If they have a little money put by, most tax-evaders pay their fines rather than complete a prison sentence; only rarely are the authorities faced by a prisoner with no desire to mitigate his punishment.

The Native Commissioner rang me up one morning. 'Listen, doctor, when you've a moment, come round and see me, will you? I've a bit of a problem up here.'

'The position is this,' he explained when, an hour or so later, I went round to his office, 'there's an old fellow in the jail that the police have brought in for not paying his taxes. He says he won't pay, because God has told him not to.'

'What do you want me to do about it?' I asked. 'Countermand those orders?'

'What I want from you is some sort of opinion as to the man's mental state; is he mad, inspired or just foxing?' The Commissioner looked at me, his eyebrows raised a little. It was clear enough what he wanted; a way out. Knowing I shared his weakness for eccentric old men with divine missions, he was looking to me to find it for him.

'All right,' I said, 'I'll go and see him for you.'

The prisoner was a slightly snuffy but extremely dignified old man with a prophet's hair-do and a flashing eye. He stood in front of me in a manner which made me feel slipshod and altogether worldly. 'I understand that you are in prison for not paying your taxes?' I asked him.

He bowed his assent.

'Would you care to tell me why you don't pay your taxes like other men?'

'I have been told not to pay them.' There was no arrogance in his reply.

'Who told you?'

'God,' he answered. I wished the gaoler were not standing listening to this interview.

'You come from Mahlabatini, don't you?' I mentioned a district seventy-odd miles from our own. Again he gave a little bow.

'What are you actually doing up here?'

'I am come to preach the gospel to all who will hear me,' he said, simply, and again I felt uncomfortably worldly; his tone carried conviction.

'Who feeds you, and where do you sleep?'

'I sleep in the homes of believers; they give me my food.'

I catechized him for a while on the message he preached, but his orthodoxy was rigid and his knowledge of the scriptures humiliating.

When I went back to the Native Commissioner he only had one word for me: 'Well?'

'I'm sure I don't really know what to say, sir. He made me feel rather a heretic.'

'But is he mad or not?'

I coughed. Forced thus into a corner I gave judgment for the prisoner. 'I have an idea that if we locked him up now, sir, we should probably have locked up Saint Paul if we'd lived a few centuries earlier; and you remember that Paul's jailers had rather a rough time of it.'

The Commissioner had been well brought up. 'What do you want me to do, then?'

'I was wondering, sir, if we could just ask him to preach somewhere else for a while . . . ?'

Thus, the district lost a prophet, but the prophet retained his honour; and so, for that matter, did the Native Commissioner.

2

The assault cases—and we are never long without admitting a broken head or a stabbed chest into the wards—are characterized by their ferocity and the complete lack of any subsequent bitterness between the victim and his assailant. Tempers, brittle with drink, rise over the most trivial things, and as quickly settle again. With the evaporation of the fumes of the party, animosity dies away, but by this time the victim is usually in hospital and his enemy in gaol. Since I attend in one or other capacity to the needs of both, I am often asked to convey greetings from the hospital bed to the prison cell; in return, sincere inquiries are made about the progress of the other's wounds; will he get well? Will he have to stay long in the hospital?

Expressions of righteous anger on our part are often gently rebuked by the sufferers as being out of place and showing a lack of charity. I expressed disgust at a brutal injury from an axe which had disfigured the face of a woman patient. 'You mustn't think too badly of him, doctor,' she said loyally of her lover who had made the attack, 'it was only a little axe he used.'

The astonishing lack of motive behind many of these crimes reflects an impetuous attitude to the whole of life. So little planning goes into even the very business of keeping alive; so few precautions are taken to avoid disaster; so little discipline is demanded of the young or expected in the old, that sudden accesses of rage—to which, alas, all men are prone—are given free rein. Two women were walking along a narrow track over the limitless grasslands, approaching each other. 'Get out of the path,' demanded the one. 'Get out of it yourself,' replied the perfect stranger. There were, no doubt, other words exchanged, but this was the only cause of the fight that we were told out of the bleeding mouth of the one who lost it. Her bottom lip was gone, bitten clean off by the other lady, presenting us with a formidable surgical problem which necessitated for her a stay in hospital of almost equivalent duration to the other's prison sentence.

In addition to the apparent purposelessness of many of the crimes of violence which are committed every year, there is also an element of chance about their results. One man, warding off a blow, has his arm broken; another, a little slower in his reactions, is killed outright by an equal knock on his unprotected skull. Giving medical evidence in countless

assaults and scores of murders, I have been impressed by the understanding that courts, high and low, show towards episodes of violence
of this kind. Benign old men shuffle into the dock to face charges of
assault with Intent to do Grievous Bodily Harm; young women face trial
for stabbing their lovers; always they can depend on justice tempered by
understanding and a liberal allowance of mercy. The facts of the assault
are seldom in dispute; it is the motive that is on trial, and the motive
usually has dwindled away to nothing in the weeks of waiting for the
hearing. The court, accepting that most of these crimes arise rather from
brief, uncontrolled anger than from calculated mischief, gives its
judgments and tempers its sentences accordingly. In more than fifty murder
trials I have known only one man to be sentenced to death, and even then
doubts of his sanity led to a reduction of the penalty to life imprisonment.

An elderly man's body was found early one morning outside his home.
I was asked to go and establish the cause of death which was supposed to
have resulted from a violent assault upon the old man. Both from the
quantity of large rocks scattered about, some of which were blood-
stained, and the unusual number of broken bones—the skull was smashed
in, as was the chest, and most of the limb bones were fractured—it was
apparent that whoever had stoned the man to death had felt very strongly
about him indeed. Everybody seemed to know who had done the murder
and the young man made no attempt to hide himself but owned rather
to a sort of pride in having rid his family of a dangerous enemy. He had
been up at work in Johannesburg when news had come of his father's
death back at his home. He had consulted Diviners who had told him of a
certain old man, once a friend of his father's but now turned against him,
who had destroyed his father by witchcraft. As soon as he was free from
his contract he had come down and killed the wizard; it was not murder,
but a just act of retribution. This, with legal modifications, was the view
taken by the court, which imposed a moderate sentence for manslaughter,
reducing the original charge on the grounds of the prisoner's lively faith
in the power of magic to kill his father.

Post mortem examination has to be carried out on all who die violent
or unexplained deaths. Very few murders are done in convenient places
or near roads, and more often than not the examination has to be made
after a long and tiring journey to some lonely or inaccessible corner of
the district. The examinations are performed on the bare ground, single-
handed or, at best, with only a policeman to assist. There is no possibility
of privacy. They are back-breaking, unseemly and, in obscure cases, often
inconclusive.

The first step is to remove the body from the position in which it has been found and place it, so far as possible, in the shade and hidden from the prying of curious eyes. The silent, grieved women sit by themselves during the examination, well away from the body, and cause no offence. With the men it is different; unless they are actively dismissed they will sit and watch the whole gruesome procedure on sons or fathers, neighbours or friends, with equal detachment. I always try to insist on all but the identifying witness being sent away, but there usually remains a hard core of two or three tribal elders who watch, solemnly and critically, from the moment of my making the long incision to the tying of the last stitch.

On hot summer days, putrefaction begins in a few hours and these autopsies can be very disagreeable. It takes time for the news of the body's discovery to reach the authorities, and though the headmen make what haste they can, two or three days may pass before the District Surgeon can reach the cadaver. Occasionally I have arrived to find myself in competition with fresh-water crabs, burying beetles and sizzling maggots for possession of the body.

Less often the first whispers of suspicion are heard after the funeral is over, and, where there is reasonable doubt about the mode of death, exhumation is ordered. The Zulu form of burial is to dig the conventional six-foot grave and then to hollow out from one wall of the pit a little chamber in which the body can be placed, reverently covered with a blanket. The chamber is closed by a woven grass mat, against which are placed flat stones, ensuring that no earth shall directly touch the body. This all makes exhumation less difficult, but does little to make it more pleasant; nevertheless a surprising amount of information can be obtained by examination even months after death.

The informer who told the police in May that Esau Mathebula had been murdered in March and quietly buried, was probably acting from spite against the man who, he said, had hit Mathebula on the head with a stone and killed him. It is not clear why he took so long about imparting this information, but after hearing the story the police obtained an exhumation order and took me along to settle the matter. The scalp injury was there, all right, but it was a slight one and must have been almost healed at the time of Mathebula's death. Most of the internal organs were nasty, limp ghosts of their former firm loveliness and the lungs had turned to greyish water; all except the lower lobe on the right hand side which had survived ten week's putrefaction almost unchanged. It was solid and still showed unmistakable pneumonia, which was quite enough to have led to his death.

3

Nor are all the deaths which have to be investigated the result of human violence. The District Surgeon is usually asked to examine the bodies of those killed in accidents or who have met death suddenly and unexpectedly from one of those strange occurrences which insurance companies—but not theologians—ascribe to an 'Act of God.'

Being mountainous and on the wet side of the Drakensberg, the district is subject to severe thunderstorms which kill by lightning-stroke three or four people each year. Travellers are the most vulnerable, caught walking or riding before they reach shelter from the storm, but less often a bolt will enter a house killing one or more of those inside and frightening the others almost beyond the point of endurance. For these arbitrary disasters, magic is not surprisingly blamed and certain powerful medicine-men are credited with the power to bring down lightning on their enemies 'out of a clear sky.'

There was confirmation in the death of Austin Sithomo for any chosen theory of magic or fatalism. Discharged from hospital after a short illness, he missed the bus which would have taken him home in the morning. 'Don't worry,' I said, 'I'm going that way this afternoon and I'll take you along.' He was thankful for the opportunity and said a cheerful good-bye when I set him down a mile from his home. Rain was just beginning to fall.

The telephone rang as soon as I got back to the hospital. A man had been killed by lightning where I had been. 'What was his name?' I asked, knowing the answer before the words came back : 'Austin Sithomo.'

But my preoccupation as District Surgeon was not wholly with death, for I was supposed—single handed as far as the Government was concerned—to keep at bay infectious disease and halt the ravages of venereal disorders throughout the district. In former times treatment of the latter was by a series of injections of an arsenical compound given weekly or as often as the patients could be persuaded to attend. The injections were given into the vein, and any accidental leakage into the tissues produced a painful brawny swelling which discouraged the patient from any further attendance. Defaulters were in the majority anyhow, no matter how skilled the injector, for the course was supposed to last for two years at least. Injections were popular, but not indefinitely.

The introduction of penicillin for the treatment of syphilis, even though it fell short of being perfect, has proved to be near enough to the practical answer to give encouragement both to the patient and his physician. A week or ten days is now sufficient for the almost certain cure of early syphilis and most patients are ready to endure this much discomfort for so glittering a prize as cure. So effective is the new treatment and so applicable to the African situation with all its disappointments, that the rate of positive blood tests among young women coming for antenatal examination fell in five years from one in four to less than six per cent; in a further three years the figure has fallen below the four per cent mark. It is unlikely that in the same period of time the morals of the community have so dramatically improved, and migrant labour takes as many young men as ever from the companionship of their wife's sleeping-mat. The cure, dramatic as it is, does not reach the more fundamental sickness of society itself.

Smallpox is rare—rarer than we have any reason to hope. Lay vaccinators do excellent work, reaching a good proportion of the people from year to year, and on the whole, vaccination is considered a sensible thing to accept on behalf of your children. There are, of course, the usual objectors, some imported more or less directly from the flourishing English stock of anti-vaccinationists, together with those who receive more individual guidance on the matter from Sources higher than the Department of Health. The only notable outbreak we have had was among a group of families of the antivaccinationist persuasion, but they were fortunately only mildly affected and there were no deaths.

Inoculation drives against typhoid fever and diphtheria are undertaken whenever there is a threat of outbreak. The response to the announcement of a free injection is so satisfactory as to raise doubts of the sincerity of so sudden and complete an acceptance of the idea of preventive inoculation. I decided to test this sincerity before embarking on the huge, milling crowd of men, women and children who had come to receive their injections at the Government's expense. I walked down the queue. 'Do you know what this injection is for?' I asked the headman. He was an officious, burly man, ostentatiously setting a good example to his followers by being first in the line. 'Of course I do; make me strong.' He gave me a knowing look and winked as man to man.

'And you, grandma, what have you come for?' She grasped my hand in her skinny fingers—they were warm and dry and hard as a fowl's claw—and pressed it to each of her shoulders in turn. 'Give me two, doctor, here and here; make my pains better.'

I passed on down the line and from the first six aspirants received six answers—all different, all wrong.

It is no part of a doctor's job to make judgments; I started at the head of the queue.

CHAPTER FOURTEEN

The Dread Sickness

I

CASES of advanced tuberculosis used to come into hospital emaciated, sweating and redolent of warm biscuits. For a week or two they lingered, spitting blood and pus from rotting lungs, and then died. We took them in only to ease their going, and to reduce, if we could, the number of those in their homes who would catch the infection before they finally succumbed.

That was before the newer tuberculostatic drugs changed the whole outlook. Now, nearly every case of tuberculosis that is admitted, even the pitiful bags of bones that come in apparently moribund from the least sophisticated homes, may expect to get better.

Although it is not an outstandingly infectious disease, tuberculosis will still spread disturbingly fast if the conditions are right for it to do so. Where there is deficient diet; where there is overcrowding; where the sterilizing sunlight is denied access to living quarters; there the soil is right for its dissemination. Hoicked out by the old men, rubbed into the earth floor by the knuckles of insanitary old women who have never heard of Robert Koch or Louis Pasteur, the bacillus will lie in the dust, dangerous as a snake, ready to be breathed into the children's lungs or licked from unwashed fingers at meal-times. Thus tuberculosis becomes a family disorder, a gift to the younger generation from the lungs of the elders. It is kissed upon the babies in the very tenderness of mother-love and handed down in the daily commerce between a father and his sons. Its entry is secret and the first manifestations of its coming are often so delayed that it may be difficult to trace the source of the infection or the time of its introduction.

Once past the sentries, the germ attacks and destroys any tissue with which it comes in contact. It sets up a violent reaction locally and sends a flame of fever through the body, giving the eye a false brightness and setting the pulses racing. Each night, in the hours before dawn, the fever burns low, almost quenched in cold sweat, but with the coming of day it mounts again. Swinging thus between extremes of temperature the body wastes its resources alarmingly fast. The daily intake of food becomes insufficient to maintain weight and energy and the body draws upon its own tissues to supply the deficit. Within a few weeks, unless it is checked, the disease-process ends in death.

Florid cases are easy to recognize, but there are others less obvious in which the diagnosis remains at first hidden, either from the mildness of the symptoms or because the essentially tuberculous nature of the disease is masked by the signs of malnutrition. Children admitted for unrelated conditions are often found to be tuberculous, though it took us nearly five years to realize just how often this was so. We learned to screen all children with a skin test and X-ray the positive reactors.

Even with the new drugs it still takes a long time to get well. Streptomycin and isoniazid have shown themselves to be powerful weapons which, used wisely, can almost guarantee victory, but to do so they must be given in full doses over many months and without intermission. They neither do away with the need for bed-rest in the early stages of the disease, nor do they do anything to heal the damaged tissues. When they have done their work, and the last tubercle bacillus is rooted out, the slow processes of healing have still to be accomplished.

It is this length of time that leads to most of the difficulties in the management of tuberculosis. Within a few weeks of his admission, the patient will have put on weight and lost his fever; he will feel well, perhaps for the first time for months, and on X-ray examination there will be objective evidence of improvement in his lungs. His new feeling of well-being, the natural wish to be among his own people and, most of all, financial anxiety may prompt him at this stage to think of his return home.

Because wages are low and the standard of living at an elementary level it does not follow that there is no hardship when the breadwinner has to spend months in hospital. Rather, the small reserve of his savings makes the problem more acute. We can do almost nothing to relieve his family. For those totally and permanently disabled a small dole can be obtained and men under treatment may be excused payment of poll-tax, but for most there is no help available at all. For us to lend money is foolishness; it is also inevitable. We make patients sign I.O.U.s which they do not understand and which we lose, but which make us feel unsentimental and businesslike, and most of those who accept loans pay back months later when we have forgotten the debt. But loans on a small scale do not solve the real problems and his family's want may drive a man to take his discharge dangerously early.

And, in truth, many could be treated as out-patients while engaged in paid work, were there the slightest hope of their conscientious attendance or any expectation of the home circumstances and diet being satisfactory. But these conditions are seldom met, and few patients are really convinced of the need for continuing treatment. In spite of formal teaching, in spite of cajoling, in spite of bullying, in the face of the clearest possible demonstrations of the penalty of defection, patients continue to default. Where they are in regular employment or under the discipline of a boarding school or hostel it may be possible to ensure regular attendance through the good offices of the employer or the schoolmaster, but as free agents, most forget or forbear to return.

Default means almost certain relapse and with the resurgence of his disease the patient becomes again infectious to others. It may even be argued that by creating a class of patients who are still infectious but well enough to get about, the new treatments are doing as much to spread the disease as to cure it.

But in spite of disappointments, two-thirds of those admitted stay the full course and are discharged at the end, their disease arrested, to continue as out-patients. One case in ten dies and the remaining quarter take their own discharge. Some of these depart in a huff, disgruntled and inclined to recrimination; others slip their moorings at night, quietly and often without any warning that they were restless or dissatisfied; others, again, go for a week's holiday and never return.

By no means all who leave hospital against advice come to any harm by doing so. A few leave within a day or two of their expected discharge date, fearful perhaps that we shall change our minds at the eleventh hour and try to keep them. These turn up at clinic and are duly registered as out-patients, nor do they subsequently default any more regularly than those who leave in the more dignified manner of formal discharge. But there are those whose departure is their undoing; who are, perhaps, ashamed and afraid to return when they see their mistake. We hear of their deaths months later in the common gossip of our neighbours.

Those who return we take back, but it is not always possible a second time to destroy the resurgent bacteria or to fill out the emaciated frame, for by this time the disease is entrenched behind barricades of fibrous tissue through which the drugs can hardly penetrate. Some default a second or even a third time, but on their return are usually beyond all aid and die; an object lesson from which nobody appears to learn anything.

Parents find the prospect of long separation from their children when these are found to have tuberculosis, especially hard to bear. When after skin-test and X-ray, a relatively well child is found to be infected and we have to break the news to the mother, she may counter by removing the child at once. At first we were repeatedly reminded that our mandate did not extend to any other part of the body than that originally deemed to be ill, but the slow growth of confidence has resolved most of these outbursts of parental intransigence so that it is now usually possible to retain children for further treatment on word of explanation alone. But no amount of sweet reason would hold Mrs Gasa, who knew her own mind and went her own way. Her child, a boy of four, had crippling tuberculosis of the spine, but it was not for this that he was brought for treatment. A fall in the fire had resulted in severe burns which we grafted successfully; when the burn was healed I raised the subject of the knuckle of twisted bone in the boy's back. 'Oh, I know all about that,' said Mrs Gasa complacently, 'I didn't bring him for his back, but for his burn; anyhow, he's better now and I want to take him home.' I pleaded with her, begging her to let the child stay for fear of its developing paralysis of the legs, but she was adamant. She flounced off, carrying the child with her, leaving me miserably suspended between righteous anger and hurt pride.

Sometimes we fail to keep patients not from any lack of faith in the hospital, nor from any alternative point of view about the nature of the illness, but from the workings of vanity alone. Whenever we admit a young patient to hospital and fail, by reason of the urgency of the admission to obtain the prior consent of the father, we are likely to cause offence. Our strong persuasions may well convince a frightened mother, but to the father, brought home from his work in the city by an anxious telegram, our concern for the child's welfare looks very much like one more bullying act on the part of a white man. Up there in the town he has to obey; if he expresses himself too freely he is sacked for insolence; if he acts independently he is sacked for disobedience. But here, among his family, he is free; he may do as he pleases, may judge for himself in his own affairs, may even commit folly in an all out effort to express his independence. He may like and trust the doctor; he may know that hospital is the best place for his ailing child; he might have brought the

15. *Waiting outside the clinic*

16. *The mixture as before*

child himself had he been at home to do so, but our unintentional invasion of his private parental rights may yet drive him to take action which he knows to be against the best interests of his child.

2

Out of all the hurt inside himself Thomas Gumede removed his wife and child from the hospital. That he loved them both there is no doubt at all; that he wanted the best for them is unquestioned, yet, from a desire to exert himself as a man and as an individual, he took away the one reasonable hope of their survival.

The union of Thomas and Eliza Gumede had been blessed within the first year by the birth of a son who, after a few months, sickened and died. It was sixteen years before Mrs Gumede again became pregnant and wisely she sought advice, coming into hospital in her last month to be near whatever help she might need. She was by this time overweight, a little breathless and all of forty years of age. The danger signals were out and we watched her carefully against the day of her labour. In her neck we found a few tell-tale lymph glands, enlarged, firm, not noticeably painful, but which were indications enough for a search for other evidences of tuberculosis. X-ray of her chest revealed active disease and we began treatment just before that happy day on which, by Cæsarean section, Mrs Gumede was safely delivered of a live boy.

Ten days is the usual time of post-natal stay for a maternity case, giving opportunity to teach the elements of infant care to women whose mothers-in-law hold strong and contradictory views to those of the hospital. It is a long enough time for practical purposes, but on occasions it is not long enough. For Mrs Gumede things did not go smoothly and even had they done so we should have had difficulty in persuading her that the painless lumps in her neck were symbols of a much graver illness in her lungs. She became restless at ten days and frantic at a fortnight.

With an outward show of reasonableness Thomas Gumede arrived on the fifteenth day. 'About my wife, doctor.'

'Yes?'

'We have an important feast at home which I wish her to attend.'

'When is that?' He mentioned a date a few days ahead. 'She's not ready to go home yet, you know,' I told him.

He countered: 'It is most important according to our custom that she should be there.'

'Look, Gumede,' I said patiently, 'you've waited seventeen years to have this child. Now you have him, safe and sound, can't you be reasonable and wait until I say he's fit to leave the hospital?'

He was unctious, flattering and unyielding. 'I am very grateful to the doctor—we all like to have him to see us when we are sick, but the doctor must understand that our customs are very strict, she must be present at the feast.'

I lost my temper first. 'For heaven's sake don't be a fool, man,' I raved, 'this is your child that I'm trying to help you to save and you come here bleating about some abominable custom which you ought to have left behind with your skins when you put on trousers.'

Gumede looked pained. All the advantages were with him. 'I understand the doctor's view perfectly, but I'm afraid my wife must be at home for the feast.'

Even this late I tried to recover my manners. 'Look, Gumede,' I said, 'I will take your wife home to the feast in the ambulance and then, when it is all over, I'll bring her back here again with me.'

'It is our custom that she should sleep at home for the night of the feast, it is quite essential,' he insisted.

'All right, then; will you agree to her coming back here if I fetch her the day after the feast?'

'Yes, I'll promise that.'

'Really?'

'Yes, really.'

So, reluctantly, we had to let him go, followed by his wife with the baby slung on her back. To match his jaunty triumph we could only muster a sense of despair and most unchristian distaste.

Two days later we sent the ambulance. Gumede saw it coming over the grassland, was seen to lock the door of his house, slip the key into his pocket and walk away. The driver wisely came home without creating a scene; Gumede's pride was satisfied even though trust lay broken and the long-deferred hope in a woman's heart faded with the intensification of her cough.

3

While confined to bed, a period of three months in most cases, the women are easier to amuse than the men. They sit in bed; they talk; they sing traditional songs on weekday nights and on Sundays draw out hymn tunes into endless dirges. At one time they will be seized with a burning desire to make grass mats; at another time to crochet; at another to thread beads or to knit. Those who have not the skills when they come, learn them from their neighbours; only rarely do they acknowledge defeat in tears like the middle-aged lady who was sure she would not be able to knit because, as she explained, 'She had only just become a Christian.'

The men are much less versatile and lie long hours in desultory talk with their neighbours, resistant to being taught skills. A few mend shoes or do leather-work from which they can earn a modest income even while staying in bed, but an attitude of distrust is adopted by the majority towards these pastimes. 'If I get any good at mending shoes you will keep me here to work for you,' said one man.

Mobility suits the men better. Their recreations are interminable games of cards, draughts and an African version of the ancient Continental game of 'The Mill.' It does not seem to matter that the pack of cards is missing a few of its less important members, for the game makes up in noise and vigour what it lacks in intellectual subtlety. The cards, lifted high in the air, are slammed down on the blankets in a flurry of dust, fluff and, I suspect, tubercle bacilli, to the accompaniment of shouts of triumph and laughter. If any one wins I am not sure, watching the game, who it is, or when is the moment of victory.

'The Mill,' played with stones or beer-bottle caps on a field sketched on a fragment of ceiling-board, is a more intelligible game and one which any African over the age of ten can depend on winning from any European rash enough to try his skill. It is the same with draughts at which most patients are humiliatingly good.

When they are allowed up—official sanction being expressed in the award of a pair of trousers—the patients are given graded occupations for limited periods in the day for which they receive pocket money. It is not very much, but it provides tobacco and small additional comforts and even in some measure allays the spectre of poverty. Half the stipend is kept in the bank so that a man is discharged with a few pounds in his pocket with which to start anew. In our turn we get the hospital windows cleaned and the litter, which falls in a daily snowstorm over the property, swept away.

Six months and longer gives sufficient time for personal eccentricities to make themselves felt, so that it is not surprising that there should arise, from time to time, ward Napoleons with real or imaginary grouses, and private Billy Grahams breathing out threatenings and slaughter on fellow-sufferers too ill to defend themselves.

Prinsloo was from mixed stock. In the South African racial hierarchy he was classified as a Coloured man and thus set a little lower than the white Angels, but lumped, for political and franchise purposes, with the whole diverse population of Indian Muslims, Hindus, Chinese, Malays, Zulus, Xhosas and Bushmen as a Non-European. He shared with his fellow Non-Europeans a common ban on the finer achievements of the white world—its concerts and plays, its architectural delights and academic opportunities—but was privileged above the others in having unrestricted access to alcoholic liquor. To this privilege and to his father's name he remained faithful; the latter his inalienable right, the former a recurrent solace.

Prinsloo's tuberculosis was extensive and chronic, but not such that it made him feel particularly ill. He was moderately obedient during the daytime but spent confused evenings in the Coloured Bar at the back of the hotel. From these visits he returned exalted to a supper long grown cold which he would, when the black mood was upon him, fling out of a window or, worse, at his unoffending next door neighbour. I would be called to reprimand an angry Prinsloo. Pointing to a pile of porridge on the drive he would assume a hard-done-by air. 'Nobody!' He would wave an arm to the listening heavens. 'Nobody! Nobody!'

'Yes?' I tried to jerk him out of the groove.

'Nobody . . . could eat that muck.'

I had a certain sympathy for him; it was not agreeable as it lay. 'If you had been here when it was served it would have been quite nice.'

But he was not paying much attention. 'Nobody . . .' he began again, but I forestalled him. 'Prinsloo, Attention!' I commanded in a sergeant-major's voice. He had been in the First World War and the conditioned reflex had not weakened in nearly forty years; he sprang to his feet in rigid attention. 'Sirr.'

'Get into bed and shut up; and don't let me hear anything more of you to-night.'

'Sirrr.' The autonomous balance which he had achieved under the stimulus of the order, drained away; his legs liquified and he crumpled on the bed and lay quiet all night.

He was regular in attendance at the yearly carol service held at eight-thirty every Christmas Eve. Modestly he took his place at the back and with spiritous fervour added loud amens wherever they were required and in a number of other places where they were not. His singing, had one been ungracious enough to listen carefully, was a variation on the original carol, innocent of actual words but strongly religious in tone. Since even human ears could sense the formless, fuddled devotion behind these anthems, I have no doubt that they were also heard in heaven.

When sober he was cheerful and hard working. He was a genius with the soldering iron and earned pocket money by mending leaks in sterilizers, jugs and other utensils. When, while under treatment for his lung tuberculosis, he developed acute appendicitis and had to have an operation, he showed that he also possessed fortitude and courage, for I never knew a more cheerful victim and it took more than a painful wound to keep him even reasonably quiet.

4

For the treatment of tuberculosis the Department of Health is prepared to pay in full. Their methods of refund—for all payments are retrospective —are tortuous and characterized by that official caution that makes of any Government department an uncheerful giver, but without their help it would be impossible to survive at all. After many letters had passed, they generously accepted a seven-eighths responsibility for the building of a tuberculosis wing for women. True, there were a number of conditions; the building and equipment had not to total more than £150 for each bed; nothing was to be purchased without officially accepted tenders; and the whole project had to be completed within the financial year which, at the time of their offer, had only nine months to run.

The sheer impossibility of the first and third conditions and the irritating lack of confidence revealed in the second, goaded us—as perhaps it was meant to do—into ant-like activity. Six days before the end of the year we had paid all our accounts and sent them in for refund. With fourteen days in hand we had the patients installed in a spacious, airy ward gay with turquoise paint and scarlet blankets.

We were all delighted; the nurses joined in the pleasure of working under such excellent conditions, and had the patients shown the same pleasure our happiness would have been complete. To our dismay they looked bored and seemed dispirited; almost daily there were pleas to be allowed home. 'What's wrong with them, Charge?' we asked the senior nurse.

'I'm not sure, doctor, they don't say.'

We left it at that, certain that we should hear more if we waited for a while, and sure enough within a few days the Charge nurse asked to speak to Margaret.

'It's because it's all so different,' she explained. 'You see, in the general wards where they were before there were lots of other patients. Every day there was something new, patients being admitted, cases back from the operating theatre, people having transfusions and so on. Now they say it is not the same; nobody ever dies and nobody ever goes home. And,' she added as her personal contribution to the investigation, 'I think they find it a bit clean in here.'

CHAPTER FIFTEEN

Little Stranger

I

THE fundamental problem in midwifery is to assist the passage of the firm though moldable infant head through the bony funnel of the mother's pelvis. The art of midwifery lies in the intelligent anticipation of the difficulties of this descent, by assessment of the hardness and size of the baby's head and the proportions of the pelvic basin.

The capacity of the latter cannot be judged from outward appearances; the generous backsides of the Zulu ladies—and we live in a world where the buttocks rather than the bosom are symbols of femininity—conceal a boyish bony structure within which straitened Western beauties might envy, but which represents a lurking peril when it comes to parturition. Fortunately there is some compensation for this disadvantage; Zulu babies are, on average, slightly smaller and lighter than English ones.

There exists a strong emotional prejudice that African women, living natural lives—for what that expression is worth—can expect to have their babies easily, painlessly and without danger; even, if the full legend is to be believed, without loss of their masters' working time. 'Man, I tell you it's no trouble to them,' say the farmers, 'they just get down behind a bush and there you are!' A few minutes after this the mother gets up, takes her hoe again and continues to work her way down between the pumpkins.

Controlled observation tells an altogether less satisfactory story. It is a tale of nature's advantages thrown away by meddlesome practices, of loss of infant life, of prolonged suffering and permanent damage in the train of ignorance and filth. Yet, given good circumstances, given protection from the wise-women, given a trustful, panic-free frame of mind, the world has no finer parturient than an African woman. A strong, splendid body and a lack of inhibition give her all the advantages if her attendant can but help her to use them.

2

Marriage, with its preliminaries of lobolo, comes later than might be expected, so that relatively few women have their first baby under the age of twenty-two. There are, of course, the very young, frequently from the schools, who, by becoming mothers at fourteen, bring down the average age, but they are a smaller group than might be supposed. Polygamy has left behind it an ideal of family spacing, with two years as a proper interval between children. Women who exceed this time are subject to emotional stress; too rapid a succession sets the neighbours' tongues clacking. With two years between pregnancies, large families are the rule and most women of normal fertility can expect to have at least six. But the biological laws which govern fish and bird operate still for man, even if in sophisticated communities he has learnt to modify their effects. The heavy corollary of having six is that we bury two or three of them; and that is only a cold way of expressing the fear and the heartache that accompanied this frequent parturition.

Out of every hundred pregnancies, only fifty-four children can be expected to survive into adult life. Out of every hundred babies born alive, more than one-third will not reach the age of puberty.

Birth itself, instead of initiating new life on earth, is only too often the moment of its extinction; it is the time of the heaviest losses, but it is also the time when we may attack most successfully and win the most resounding victories over this waste. With the victories that attend even the simple facilities available in country hospitals, will arise many new problems; problems of feeding the survivors; problems of birth control and family spacing. In solving these questions society may have to turn itself upside down. And that may not be wholly a bad thing.

Even in an imperfect social system; even with the infant mortality around three hundred and fifty for each thousand live births, each new pregnancy is a source of rejoicing. No resultant poverty; no disgrace of illegitimacy; not even the physical strain of repeated childbearing can for long suppress the bubbling satisfaction of a new pregnancy. There are, of course, exceptions; the poor hearts and the habitually melancholy, but the primeval complacency of the womb is stronger than most other emotions, which makes the moralist's task a hard one and his way thorny.

Young women who have retained tribal dress announce their pregnancy by covering their breasts with a hanging, buckskin pinafore, beautifully decorated with beads, while their more modern sisters wear the wide skirts and three-quarter length maternity garments whose function is only in part to hide the swelling curves. All alike share the same desire to publish their condition.

3

Many who come to the antenatal clinic are unable to count for themselves and come to hear of their progress with each passing month. Until the last six weeks, unless anything is amiss, we ration attendance to once a month for fear of establishing a morbid outlook among the women. Almost none know when the whole process began so that we have developed a fair degree of skill at guessing, but there are many sources of error and it is seldom possible to be more accurate than two weeks either way. Occasionally, having delivered a verdict, it will be hotly and indignantly denied. 'Impossible! My husband was not even at home five months ago.' Suitable adjustments are made hastily, as they had to be with the young woman who was so sure of her dates. 'I'm not seven months, doctor, I'm only five.'

'Oh? How do you make that out? Can you count?'

'No, doctor.'

'Then how do you know . . .?'

'My husband has been to school; he counts for me.'

A sturdy disregard for probabilities leads several older women into errors which are not wholly without pathos. The desire for just one more baby before it is too late makes a few misinterpret the natural drying of the wellsprings of reproduction as the first indications of pregnancy, even after a suspiciously long period of time. So it was with the Diviner Nobutakathi who consulted me after two years as to when she might expect her baby? 'My good woman,' I expostulated from the ivory tower of rationality, 'surely you know you can't be pregnant for two years?'

'*I* can,' she came back, quick as a flash. '*I* can. I was five years carrying my last one, *and* I had a live baby at the end of it.'

With so much uncertainty over dates the formal booking for hospital —if that is the choice for delivery—becomes a mere matter of opinion. Both the patients and ourselves prefer that they come within our orbit early rather than late, we because it reduces to a minimum ambulance calls at the dead of night, they because it means early release from the claws of predatory mothers-in-law who are not above keeping their sons' wives working about the home until the latest possible moment.

But there are disadvantages in their early arrival. They are not admitted as patients, yet they require housing and feeding. They are unspeakably idle, content to stuff themselves with food and sit, indolent as cats in the sun, adding a perimeter of fat to the babies in their wombs and slackening their belly muscles.

This monumental laziness is, moreover, against custom. A Zulu baby is traditionally credited with making for itself a contribution to the total expulsive effort required at the time of its delivery. If its mother has been idle, in like measure the infant will make no serious effort to crawl forth into the world. But for most of the women, present food and sunshine holds more attraction than any theoretical risk attached to this laziness, and they continue to eat and sit save when goaded by the staff into flickering activity. Nor, on any account, can the waiting days be occupied in preparing for the baby's arrival, for to do so would be to tempt brittle fortune to breaking point. All the sewing, all the buying of little bonnets and bootees, must await the safe arrival and survival of the infant. In this apparent improvidence there are two advantages; no money is wasted if the child is stillborn; and the choice of a suitable colour, pink for a girl and blue for a boy, can be deferred until the sex of the child is known, thus resolving the dilemma of the European woman who tries to guess. But any advantages are outweighed by the sudden realization and consequent panic that the child must be fitted out at least one day before discharge from hospital. We are compelled to provide baby clothes for the ten days of the lying-in, but after that our responsibility ends. Tearful ladies find they have no money for cloth or knitting wool and to-morrow the baby is about to be turned out, naked, into the world. We have counselled forethought until we are exhausted, but the pattern repeats itself over and over again.

4

Those who, by accident, pigheadedness or pride leave their admission over until the last minute, and then call the ambulance, frequently run into difficulties. Under no circumstances can a woman, once she is in labour, be removed from her home for fear of the baby's arrival when and where all is unprepared. Thus, ambulance calls for maternity cases often lead to hair-raising journeys with, at their end, the alternatives of inextricable disaster on the one hand, or the bathos of a born-before-arrival on the other. There are some who are found to be not in labour at all, and a few whose return to the hospital is an anxious race against the sweeping wingbeats of the stork.

The gamp in charge of the woman in the back of the ambulance was screaming and banging on the cab window. 'It's coming! Quick, doctor! Oh! Quick!' I stopped the car and felt in the cubby hole for the torch; it was missing. Outside it was completely dark, no stars, no moon, not a ray of light from anywhere. Leaving the headlamps burning I jumped out and ran round to the back. The gamp was about right; we had not stopped any too soon. I fumbled in the bag but could find nothing I wanted in that inky blackness. My travelling companion was wearing a white dust coat. He knew nothing of obstetrics but perhaps he could help a little. 'Get out in front of the lights,' I shouted to him. He obeyed and by the pale illumination from his coat where he stood, moon-like out there in front, the woman was safely delivered of a live baby.

At home, giving birth is a corporate affair, offering the womenfolk unrivalled opportunity for gossip, curiosity and neighbourly interference. In the smoky atmosphere of the home, by the dim light from the oily flame of a paraffin wick, the mother lies sprawling, bound by a cruelly tight binder, washed by the chatter from the audience. Any delay, from whatever cause, is judged the result of her cowardice and the taunts of the onlookers urge her to still further expulsive efforts. Further delay means for her the introduction of the questing, unwashed fingers of the older women, seeking something on which to pull, looking for obstacles in the way of descent. They widen the passages, cutting the tender flesh with a razor blade or a fragment of broken glass. Yet, so wonderful is the mechanism of birth, so precise, so co-ordinated, that the majority of babies slip through this cordon of terrible assistance into life, squalling and hideous but incredibly dear.

Twin births, traditionally unwelcome in Zulu society, are nevertheless about twice as frequent as they are among white women. The accepted belief is that the father's life is forfeit if both twins survive. And fathers in former days took no chances—there were enough hazards in their rough lives without adding to them by neglect of custom—and disposed of at least one of the pair. It was done without guilt, in the unemotional manner of the soldier who knows that a certain price in human life must be paid for a desired end. It was a common-sense precaution which a man would be ill-advised to neglect.

In modern times men have become convinced that twins can be reared without any significant increase in the paternal death-rates. Christian influence, the fear of police reprisals and the beneficent teachings of the hospitals have combined to put an end to the more barbarous manifestations of twin-killing. But the battle is not over yet. Repeatedly we see twins, the one bouncing and breast-fed the other a shrivelled weasel of a child whose diet at the hands of its grandmother has been nothing more sustaining than soured maize porridge. It is hard to avoid the conclusion that the unpopular twin is farmed out to the loving and perilous care of its grandmother in confident expectation of death. It is murder most elegant, and proves remarkably effective.

In danger from gamps; with peril from magic; faced by an appalling stillbirth rate in their own homes, it is not surprising that the younger women are seeking hospital confinement in increasing numbers. Hospital may be unfamiliar and perhaps a little frightening; uniformed sisters may be forbidding substitutes for the familiar features of a mother or a dearly loved aunt, but there are many compensations. If things go ill there are anæsthetics; steps can be taken to hasten delivery if the child's life is at stake; best of all is the expectation of returning home with a live baby.

Margaret took charge of the maternity department, supervising the difficult cases, which means she has to take most of the night calls. From these excursions she creeps back into bed smelling of proprietary antiseptic—an unromantic if useful fluid. Every obstetrician must sooner or later feel that babies are all born in the middle of the night expressly for his inconvenience, and doubtless many mothers share his distaste for the pallid misery of these night vigils. Yet a sober analysis reveals that as many babies are in fact born in the daylight hours as in the night and any slight excess in the latter group may be attributed to chance alone. But these figures, however correct, can never belittle the merit of those who have to leave a warm bed on a cold night.

Infection was never a dominant fear in our minds, whether we were dealing with an emergency admitted from outside or one of our own booked cases. It occurred, certainly, and just occasionally began that fulminant course which in former days made child-bed fever the greatest single cause of maternal death. Penicillin and the sulphonamides have altered the picture so that in civilized communities the fever has lost its terror; at our level, with widely spaced houses and no village life at all, the chances of widespread infection were never great. But that did not stop Emmie Sondezi from coming in after interference at home with a high temperature and a just saveable baby. Cæsarean delivery seemed to be necessary to save her life at all, with the hope that penicillin might atone for the breaking of surgical canons against operation in the presence of infection. In a way it did, but not before the poor woman had spent four days in delirium, slipping in and out of eternity. During the ward-round on the fifth morning she began the long march back; she opened her eyes as we came to her bed, took a piece of Margaret's skirt in her hand, looked at it, tested its quality. 'That's a nice bit of cloth you've got there,' she said, and drifted away again. Penicillin, another operation and an insatiable interest in life combined to carry the day, and after five months Emmie went home to her two children. My own respect for the pus-forming organisms was in no way diminished because we had won the round; on the contrary I learnt to be actively thankful that such events were rare.

5

An obstetrical department is concerned as much with the rearing of infants as with their production. Chief among the problems is the establishment of breast-feeding. To me, the unexpected thing was how often tension rises over this natural function in African women; in my ignorance I had imagined the whole process would be automatic and perfectly free from trouble. Alas, it is not, although with persistence most women can manage wholly to support their children for at least six months. We came across a few mothers from town homes in whom breast feeding fails either from a lack of real intention—and the economic pressure to return to work operates in these women as it does in Europe—or from that failure which is seen all too commonly in highly civilized communities and which is the despair alike of the young mother and her medical adviser.

Unless influenced by the hospital, Zulu mothers do not pin their whole faith on breast feeding. 'It is not enough,' they say as they grind up the starchy part of the maize grain, from which they remove the nutritious germ, and make a thin white porridge for their babies. This gruel, which in lazy homes is permitted to grow sour, is given by means of a bottle, usually one of our medicine bottles adapted for the purpose with a teat of the mother's own devising. Flaccid, greasy, bearing a large ragged hole at the tip, the teat is the haunt of a hundred houseflies, sharing the honours with an equally unpleasant dummy for the perpetuation of infantile diarrhœas and fungus infections of the mouth and throat.

One night I was called to a home about five miles from the hospital. 'The babies are refusing their porridge,' I was told. This hardly seemed justification for a night journey, but perhaps there was more to the story than just this, so I went. A moment or two after entering the hut I was invited to see the children whose refusal of their porridge had caused so much distress. From a single blanket two tiny shrivelled infants were produced, twins, prematurely born and not totalling between them more than five pounds in weight. 'They won't swallow,' complained the old midwife, producing a greyish gruel in a bottle and plying the pink mouths afresh. I suggested that perhaps a meal of porridge on the first day was a little too much for premature infants, but was quickly shown how wrong I was. 'Oh, no, doctor, not at all; *all* her children are always fed on porridge right from birth.' But the twins' unco-operative refusal of their first meal gave me the trump card. 'I think we'd better take them up to hospital and try what we can do there,' I suggested.

The twins were nursed in a wooden box on top of the anthracite cooker. By raising the cot to a greater or lesser height above the stove a controlled temperature could be maintained. Here they flourished and grew slowly into mature babies—without the benefit of porridge in any form.

There are three principles in rearing premature infants; the maintenance of body warmth, the prevention of infection and the avoidance of fussy handling and over-feeding. In our primitive soap-box incubator, under the skilled hands of one of our nursing sisters who had herself been premature, we saved many of these tiny creatures. The nurses learnt their management and caught the enthusiasm for their survival. They became competent at coaxing the children to feed and could soon pass tubes into the babies' stomachs when they failed to swallow. It became a disgrace—as it was right that it should—to lose even the most apparently hopeless little creature, however lobster-pink the philosopher-face, however lax the tortoise-neck.

The buildings in which the hospital's maternity work is carried out are overcrowded and inadequate and under these conditions accidents are bound from time to time to occur. Of the accidents, the commonest is the bottle-burn. In theory, these burns cannot happen, for the canvas cots in which the babies are nursed have pouches for hot water bottles outside the cot altogether; in practice many babies begin life in soap cases pressed into service as cots when the official cribs are all being used. In these bottle burns are always possible. The burns are deep and shameful, leaving as they heal puckered scars as a permanent reminder of the hospital's failure. Years afterwards mothers bring their growing children and, turning them bottom-up, show me the scar .'You remember your baby, don't you, doctor? She got this at the hospital.' I do indeed remember little Busisiwe, and the tears and the inquiry into the circumstances, and my own embarrassment. I return silent thanks that the mother seems to take pride in this brand which proves so conclusively to her neighbours that this is a genuine hospital baby.

The final advice that we give to the mothers on their discharge is three-fold : to feed the baby on the breast, to eschew maize porridge, and to refrain from giving enemas every day. The advice is politely received, there are smiles and courtesies, and the women bear away their children in excited anticipation of the reception awaiting them at home. If a mother comes with us in the clinic van, she is usually met on the roadside by the grandmother; there is a little dance of glee, free as old bones will permit, followed by a thorough kissing of all parts of the little body that are not hidden by the new woollen blanket in which it is wrapped. The two women walk away with their treasure in the older woman's arms. This, after all, is the common behaviour of grandmothers the world over, and perhaps if we addressed our parting advice to them instead of to the relatively unimportant mother, it would bear more fruit. But teaching elders is unrewarding : gravely the old ladies nod their heads through our recital. 'Yes, yes, we understand you perfectly, the child is to be fed on the mother's breast. What was that? No enemas? But what if the child does not have its bowel moved? It doesn't *matter?* And no porridge? Not just a little when the mother is away visiting? What, not to visit without the baby?' They shake their heads, smiling, turning to their neighbours. 'He's so kind, and *such* a joker!' and every one laughs and nods in approval.

But I think we win some of the rounds in this unequal contest; a few babies undoubtedly only have enemas on alternate days and many—more and more every year—are wholly breast-fed.

Old Mrs Moloi was so completely converted to the new doctrines that she made her daughter-in-law bring her sick grandchild up to the hospital when it fell ill. The young Mrs Moloi was sitting sulking in the waiting room next to the impressive figure of the older woman when Margaret entered the out-patients.

'Good morning, Mrs Barker.' The old lady's greeting was cheerful and confident as between equals.

There was a murmur among the other waiting patients. 'You mustn't greet Europeans in so familiar a style,' cautioned a quiet young man from the corner of the room. 'They resent it from us.'

'Oh, that's all right,' replied Mrs Moloi airily, 'I was only addressing Mrs Barker.'

She swept into the consulting room. 'This child is ill, and I want you to admit it to hospital if you think fit.'

Margaret glanced at the young mother.

'Don't you worry about *her,*' continued Mrs Moloi. 'If you want to take the child in, just you do so.'

Much maligned, adored by their grandsons, experienced, crafty, humorous and obstinate, the grandmothers are occasionally the strongest allies that we have. If you can win a grandmother; if, taking a slow pinch of snuff, she smiles and agrees, there is not much that can go wrong thereafter.

CHAPTER SIXTEEN

Teacher or Taught?

BECAUSE, in the beginning, there was no possibility of recruiting African staff to the senior positions—we were infinitely obscure and had in any case no money for their salaries—our small community mirrored the traditional South African pattern of white leadership with a black labouring and student population, a structure which at best leads to a sterile paternalism and at worst degenerates into servility on the one hand and arrogance on the other.

Relationships between doctors and nurses, between teachers and taught, which would in England have been free and sympathetic, could not in Zululand fail to be interpreted in terms of colour. Even a hasty request in a crisis could precipitate a prolonged attack of the sulks or, worse, an angry resignation.

Margaret was asked to go to the Matron's office. 'Nurse Frances has made a serious allegation against you, Mrs Barker, and, since I'm sure there must be some misunderstanding, I wanted you to hear it from her own lips.'

Margaret looked at the offended nurse. 'If I've said or done anything I'm quite unaware of it. What did I say to you, Nurse?'

Nurse Frances hung her head and said nothing at all.

'Come along, Nurse,' urged the Matron. 'You were ready enough just now to say that Mrs Barker had insulted you. What did she actually say?'

There was another long pause and then : 'She called me a darky,' she burst out. 'A darky.'

'I've never used that expression in my life, Nurse. When did I call you a darky?'

'Yesterday, in the theatre.'

Margaret wracked her brains, but could recall nothing. 'What was I doing when I said it?'

'You were giving the anæsthetic and told me to hold the patient's arm, then you called me a dar . . .'

Light broke. 'No, no! My dear girl, not a darky; I said, "Hold the arm for me, ducky." '

Explanations and apologies followed; it was made clear that the word held no sinister meaning at all and Nurse Frances was pacified. It was true that her touchiness was exceptional. It was true that she had not a very robust personality and left hastily a few months afterwards, called, as she phrased it, to become a mother. But the hurt had been no less real for being based on a misunderstanding.

Outside the peculiar circumstances of the South African scene our attempts at finding a more excellent way of living, closer knit and free from the taint of Apartheid, must appear incredibly naïve. There is a sense that even the conscious wish to learn to live in a corporate way, ignoring the traditional divisions of colour, meant that the attempt was bound to fail, as a man may scale unaccustomed ladders for just so long as he does not look down at the ground beneath him. Yet somehow, if we were to justify our existence as a mission hospital—and there was never any expectation of matching in excellence of equipment the wealthier Government institutions—the barriers which were dividing us from one another had got to go down.

Closer companionship could not be achieved merely by desiring it, nor by a succession of interracial tea-parties; only as we came to know one another and respect one another as colleagues could there be any hope of success. That, together with the desire that we, who received the Lord's Body together, might also express that unity in everyday friendship. We had first to be quite certain that we really did desire the fall of the traditional barriers, which operated greatly to our advantage; to be quite certain that we were not using our colleagues to demonstrate to ourselves a lofty liberalism of mind; and to be sure that we were not collecting black heads round the dinner table to show that we—whatever our neighbours might say—did not care for the normal separations between black and white in South Africa.

Mere liberalism could hardly have avoided these pitfalls, but we were less concerned with liberalism than to discover a method of running a hospital which had by now become in fact a multiracial organization. As our power to pay a reasonable wage increased and as the work grew until we came to rely in most departments on senior African executives, so the multiracial nature of the hospital became more evident. On the tentative, self-conscious beginnings of our early association, we saw a more robust growth established. But the giving which made this possible has been mostly from the side of the African staff, for to their wish for a closer association they have had to add forgiveness for our racial arrogance which

17. *Dancing*

18. *Peeling pumpkins*

made the *rapprochement* necessary in the first place, while we have had to do nothing more difficult than to accept at their hands the overtures of friendship.

The lighting of even so small a candle as the establishment of a common staff mess where men and women could eat together or sit after supper by the fireside, was not accomplished without criticism from outside. To our European neighbours—whose personal goodwill and affection has been unfailing—the rejection of the customary separations gave pain rather than caused anger. True, many who before might have dropped in to tea or passed the time of day with us, felt shy or embarrassed to do so any more. Only a few continued to attend our prizegiving ceremonies or open days, but those who did gave encouragement both to the nurses and our-selves, and we remained thankful to them.

But beyond the immediate neighbourhood there was less tolerance for our breach of etiquette. When Dr Dhlamini joined the staff and came to live, a black man in close association with white women, political capital was made out of the unseemly state of affairs. It was election time when he joined us and both parliamentary parties were holding their meetings in a spirit of bitterness which, considering their racial policies were virtually identical, was surprising. The National Party speakers caught on to the idea first, pointing to the hospital as typical of what the country could expect if the United Party came into power. In this they flattered their opponents' liberality, but the story went about through the Northern Districts of Natal and caused the United Party man some embarrassment.

A few days before the poll a car drove up to the front of the hospital and a young man came to my office. 'Are you Dr Barker?' he inquired politely.

'Yes.'

'Could you spare me a moment, doctor? Somewhere private?'

I assured him we were safe enough in my office and asked him to sit down while I closed the door.

'I'm afraid what I have to say is not very pleasant,' he began.

I tried to help him on. 'No?'

'The thing is this, doctor; there have been complaints that you have a Native man living with your white sisters.'

'That is one way of putting it, I suppose,' I agreed.

'The Nats have been saying that this is the sort of thing that the country can expect if the U.P. gets in, and we're very worried about it.'

I saw his point of view. 'You can tell them that I'm not a member of
the United Party.'

'But couldn't you . . .? Just until after the election?'

'No, I don't think I could do that. Dr Dhlamini is a colleague and I'm
not going to ask him to live at the bottom of the garden.'

The interview was over to the relief, I imagine, of both of us.

'Won't you stay to lunch?' I invited, and then realized that Dr Dhlamini
would be there. I told him so. 'It's very good of you,' he smiled, shyly.
'But perhaps, under the circumstances, I'd better say no.'

The Nationalists won the election all right, but I did not feel that their
victory was wholly our fault.

The Zulu schoolboy who wrote that a missionary doctor is one who
'Prays over you before he kills you' hit upon a definition which, if less
than kind, probably reflects accurately enough the viewpoint of the man
in the street. True, its sly suggestion of inferior doctoring underpinned
by hopeful prayer is fair neither to the skill nor the piety of the individual
mission doctor, but the definition does recognize the nature of man as
more than body; as more even than mind and body alone. After a long
period of arid materialism, contemporary medicine is waking up to the
possibility that the schoolboy may be right.

In truth it is harder to think of a definition of a medical missionary
than it is to pull other people's ideas to pieces. Is he conscientious? So
are most of his colleagues. Does he work incessantly? So do most general
practitioners. Does he love his patients? The best physicians have always
done so. Does he work under adverse conditions? Others have done so
before him. Is he poorly paid? Yes, but he enjoys a measure of security
and, at the end, a pension which a working-man might envy. Even these
reasons which stem from his continued isolation—the if-I-don't-do-it-
nobody-else-will argument—are falling away. Everywhere National Govern-
ments are improving medical services and increasingly making use of heli-
copters and ambulances to carry the sick to hospitals better built and
better staffed than the missionary institutions which began the work but
under modern circumstances cannot really afford to maintain it.

Individually, then, the mission doctor is of little account and his hospital
unlikely in future to retain even the local importance that it had in the
past. Perhaps medical missionaries have always known this. Just as the
whole missionary movement, with its insistence on the building up of
an indigenous ministry, has within itself the seeds of its own ending.

Within his lifetime the young mission doctor may have to face the decay of his work. It should not discourage him; rather he may use his knowledge to check in himself any personal ambition, any desire to become a Father of the People. While he works he may remember that, whatever importance his medical knowledge gives him in the community, he is finally judged not by this but by what manner of man he is. Master in his own operating theatre, he must understand that he is a foreigner and often a servant in the outside world. What he does as a doctor is paid for; what he is as a man may make or mar his witness as a missionary and his usefulness to the local church of which he is a member.

It is as a servant of the local church—of the congregation with which he worships—that the medical missionary has such importance as is his. He is, or should be, an expression of that care for the physical man which parallels the priest's care for the spiritual man. Wherever the Church has been true to her nature this has been the mark of her dual care; which is not unexpected in a faith which accepts in the person of Jesus of Nazareth the point of entry of God into the human scene.

And if the missionary is judged, as I believe he is judged, not by what he does but by who and what he is; by his willingness to receive as well as to give; by his acceptance of his rightful place in the congregation, be that high or low, leader or servant; by his identification with the people among whom he is called to live, it follows that he must study to understand their ways and aspirations in order the more deeply to commit himself. In this decade in South Africa such identification is certainly against custom and is rapidly becoming suspect in the eyes of the law. Even where there is a genuine desire for identification, its realization is almost hopelessly difficult. The white missionary will be identified with the whites first and the missionaries afterwards, and then only in so far as he proves himself. Preoccupied by administrative detail, befriended by his fellow-whites with whom most of his leisure is spent, he becomes too busy for language-study, too self-important to risk his neck by non-compliance in the common law of Apartheid.

His very desire for better conditions of work for himself and his fellows; his zeal for 'his' church, 'his' school or 'his' hospital may themselves be the means by which he grows further from his neighbours. Otherwise worthy ambitions may so easily take precedence in his mind over the need for fearless alignment with the hopes and wishes of those with whom and for whom he is pledged to live and work. His ideals of service, his unremitting work, the selfless expenditure of his days, are meaningless if the desire for this identification is lost.

The Man Next to Me

For nothing that he can do, by the skill of his hands or the devotion of his life, can ever repay one hundredth part of the damage that, by their arrogance and greed, he and his people have caused. Only common friendship and genuine affection can be counted on the credit side; and friendship and love are in pitifully short supply between men of different colour in South Africa.

I was standing with my house-surgeon on the platform, waiting for the train. That he was an African and I a European had long since ceased to matter to either of us and we were talking together when a young man came up and spoke to him. The stranger was wearing the narrow trousers and the blazing tie of that international army of aimless, anti-social young men who puzzle sociologists, bewilder clergymen and infuriate the police from New York to Johannesburg. He spoke in a dialect I did not understand.

'What did he say to you, George?' I asked when the youth had passed down the platform. But George, normally the least inhibited of men, was not communicative. 'Nothing,' he replied. 'Just talk.'

'Come on, George, what sort of talk?'

'Oh, I don't know, he just asked me what I hoped to gain by talking with a white man.' And George looked unhappy.

What indeed? We who took the land by cunning and conquest; we who built a nation by the sweat of black brows and kept the wealth and the enjoying of it to ourselves; we who made men carry passes, herding them like cattle; we who classified men and women by the colour of their skin and made them ashamed; we who locked up the farm labourers at Bethal when their day's task was done to prevent their deserting; we who wanted men's work but denied them the right to live decently with their families near to that work; we who sought to close our universities to men of colour; we above all who have been intolerant of the poor and despised the illiterate; who have said to our brother, 'Raca, thou fool'; what good to talk as a friend to one of us?

I must have shown my discomfiture. 'Don't worry, Anthony,' George soothed, 'he was only a good-for-nothing corner-boy.'

But I was not comforted.

Nqutu, Zululand, 1958

FOREIGN MISSIONS IN THE
TWENTIETH CENTURY

The Self-Limiting Task

FOREIGN MISSIONS IN THE
TWENTIETH CENTURY

THE surest way of annoying Dr Livingstone was to ask him whether, after all, he was not more of a geographer than a missionary? 'Viewed in relation to my calling, the geographical feat is the beginning of the missionary enterprise,' he wrote in answer to the London Missionary Society which had rashly questioned his motives. We should not blame the bearded, righteous men who asked the question; theirs was a high trust— to collect the money of faithful chapel folk and, through their agents overseas, to translate that money into new congregations in heathen lands. They were thinking as reasonable men when they demanded that a certain outlay in money should produce a certain number of conversions. Here was their most famous, and certainly their most formidable, employee crossing and recrossing Africa on foot, from the Indian Ocean to the cold Atlantic shore, and where were his results? True, his journeys had caught the public imagination to make of Livingstone the unwilling scape-goat of a nation's conscience, just as men and women to-day have placed their uneasy burdens on the bowed shoulders of the illustrious Dr Schweitzer; true, his labours to break the slave trade bore, when refined at the capable, polished hands of prelates and politicians, fruit beyond his best hopes; true, his discoveries about the watersheds of Africa have been of the greatest importance in the development of that vast continent, yet in every case his work was to lay only the veriest foundations upon which the master-builders, Rhodes and Stanley, among others, had la-boriously to build. All this, the missionary society in London could hardly be expected to forsee. All that was apparent was sporadic preaching with little or no follow-up, and a nominal missionary preoccupied with his eternal wanderings, travelling for months together in the company and under the protection of the very slavers he was pledged to eradicate, spend-ing the last few, damp months of his life pushing through swamps which he hoped were the sponges of the Nile, yet feared in his heart were but the extreme hinterland of the Congo system—which they were.

He and the old gentlemen of the mission quarrelled and parted, yet he indignantly rejected an offer of funds to go back to Africa as a geographer, writing to James Young that he '. . . would not consent to go merely as a geographer, but as a missionary, and do geography by the way, because I feel I am in the way of duty when trying either to enlighten these poor people or open their land to lawful commerce.'

Livingstone was more appreciated on the continent where he worked. They brought his body down to the coast when he died, men for whom he had seemed to have little more than a sorrowing pity; men whom he was not above moulding with a whip; men who had left him alone in his extremity, and pilfered his possessions when he was disabled. They brought his body down to the coast in love, recognizing in the withdrawn, humorous, irascible man something which inspired them to show a measure of affection which has, perhaps, never again been equalled between black men and white.

Livingstone's father-in-law, Robert Moffat, was of a different order. Where the near-sightedness of the London Missionary Society irritated Dr Livingstone to the point of resignation, its faithful care for its agent in Kuruman, Dr Moffat, made of the latter one of the society's most loyal workers. 'Dear, good Mr and Mrs Moffat are so wedded to the society; it is really essential to their Christianity to believe in it,' commented their daughter-in-law Emily Moffat to her father, a sagacious tea-merchant of Bristol. The society returned Moffat's trust in themselves, assisting him in every possible way to carry out his mission to the Bechuanas. In spite of quarrels with the society's senior worker in Cape Town, Dr Philip, over the political duties of a missionary, Moffat's relations with the parent mission remained cordial. He was a preacher and a teacher of such enthusiasm that it seemed at times as if he overstepped the bounds both of propriety and ethics in reaching his hearers. For him, no holds were barred in making contact with the people. Presents—the irrepressible Emily Moffat called them by a ruder name—passed between him and the chiefs and leaders of the people, opening ears which remained deaf to the words of others who, with nicer consciences, camped on the edge of the tribal lands waiting for an invitation to enter which never came.

In their strong, diverse personalities, Livingstone and Moffat epitomized two strands in the missionary thread which has run through the development of modern Africa. The one, concerned for the over-all development of the country, onward-looking towards the future, the other the preacher, satisfied that the missionary task was first and last the conversion of the heathen masses to the Christian faith, and content for strategy to use a direct frontal attack on the barbaric mores of the time. Either method meant innumerable difficulties. How often, lonely under the night sky, hearing the frogs in chorus down at the river, must Livingstone's faith have been tested? What if he *were* really deceiving himself, seeking glory for his travels, putting the discovery of the source of the Nile above his search for fellowship with his Maker? And would not Moffat have doubts, too? He could not be forever preaching; so few came to hear him, so very few were baptized except the half-castes and the wandering Hottentots for whom, as Moffat realized, there might be certain temporal advantages in becoming Christians. Inevitably, both must have felt that they were wasting their time. Yet, as Livingstone tramped in utter silence the broad grass-lands or squelched through the swamps, was he 'wasting time' any more than Moffat who was forced to spend much of his time in his vegetable garden or with his herd of precious cattle, preoccupied with the business of staying alive in a barren land? Both of them yearned for more con-tact; everywhere men were unwilling to hear them, indifferent to the message that burned on the preachers' lips. So little, so very little, seemed to go home. 'It would be a positive relief here to get hold of somebody who was sufficiently curious to ask a single question about religion.'

These two strands were inevitably fused together as the years went by. Itinerant preaching gave way to settled missionary work within a circum-scribed area, and the Mission Station developed, peopled at first with the new converts. In the early days those who heard the call and responded to it often found themselves outside the tribal pale, banished by baptism from the closely knit kinship of the tribe. They settled on the mission lands and, in a generation or two, formed the backbone of the new con-gregations. Their children attended school and were taught—embryonic intellectuals who were to become the pioneers of a new, aware Africa. Their tuition and care took up more and more of the missionary's time until the need for reinforcement by lay missionaries, teachers and carpen-ters, doctors and nurses became imperative. It is in this multiplication of the lay missionary that the mission station of to-day most differs from the solitary preaching-unit of the early pioneers. Not that the laity were for-gotten in some of the earliest endeavours, but that they were sorely swamped by members of what Dr Livingstone described as the 'Parso tribe.' On the original, tragic expedition of the Universities' Mission to Central Africa Livingstone notes that, in addition to the five clergymen sent up the Shire River, there were: 'One carpenter—a poor stick—one shoemaker, one gardener, one printer—Europeans—and three black men, two of them noted blackguards.'

With the settling of mission stations their influence extended and their resources grew, largely in relation to the comparative wealth of the various missionary societies which controlled them. Thus were created the highly organized centres, comprising church school and hospital in a three-pronged attack on paganism, ignorance and human misery. Livingstonia, Holy Cross in the Pondo country, Adams, Lovedale and a host of others began in this way. They have been powerful witnesses and sources of much that is good.

In the process of becoming established, the missionary himself was bound to change. For one thing the new, lay missionaries were not clergy and, though they were faithful men and women for whom the command to preach the gospel and heal the sick had seemed to speak with especial distinctness, they were often less than able to put their faith into words, still less to stand up to any consistent catechism of doubt. They were people for whom the mission was seen as a work of mercy, where, of their abundance, they sought to share with the less fortunate of the world. They wished to bring healing and sight, not as a sort of secular sprat to catch the religious mackerel, but because they saw that the Divine command implied a care for the physical and intellectual, as well as the spiritual, well-being of those to whom they ministered.

Nor is it disrespectful to the Cloth to say that the ordained men were also changing. This was not wholly the result of increasing administrative burdens applied to their willing backs, although that had something to do with it, but more especially it was a changing emphasis in the Christian faith itself that altered their mode of attack. The early men, Moffat and the others, brought to their work in addition to a love of souls, a lively sense of the imminence of Hell. That from any slackness of theirs the souls of men should be lost, goaded them into phenomenal tasks and perilous journeys without any thought for themselves at all. But the physical flames of Hell seems in the twentieth century to have lost their fierce heat, and while the sense of urgency in men's salvation persists, there are fewer clergy to-day who would add to their message of the love of God a simultaneous threat of Hell to bring up the slackers from the rear. It is not that Hell has cooled, but that we are inclined in this present age to think it not quite sporting to mention it.

Much of the glamour faded from the missionary scene as the mission institutions grew in organization and influence, but the work of the missionaries took on new aspects which have been a far greater force for conversion and education than the lonely, heroic endeavours of earlier days. Christian colonies were built up whence, in spite of imperfections, something of the light of Christian charity was reflected. By that light, a growing number of boys and girls first learnt to escape from the nihilism of a magical society into a responsible view of the world and of themselves. Older folk, mostly women as in church circles the world over, grew to love the church and the faith that it preached. A few young men felt the call to the ministry and were ordained.

Somehow, out of a great deal of ill-understood education and undigested religious material, a new type of young man and young woman was being created. Here developed the new, politically aware citizens of Africa; here were women desirous of better homes and a brighter future for their children. There were plenty of failures as well, plenty for whom this new liberty of thought and action was an intolerable strain, plenty for whom the temptations of wealth and idleness were too strong, and who sank into debauchery and crime.

The greater expense of highly organized missionary work necessitated the acceptance of grants from the Government with, since he who pays the piper calls the tune, increasing Government control. In the field of education this has come, in South Africa, to mean the virtual exclusion of the missionary. Jealous of Church influence and fanatically intent on impressing their own stamp on African schoolchildren, the Nationalist Government stepped in. The missions had proved themselves too liberal in outlook—a point of view which many of their former pupils would have reason to doubt—and in most cases were incurably English in loyalty. They had taught in a muted manner that Jack was as good as his master and so let loose dangerous doctrines of racial equality which ran exactly counter to the accepted beliefs of that Government which so generously had provided most of the money.

But there was another reaction beside that of the Government towards the missions; the reaction of the pupils themselves. So many who later became powers in the land, whether as doctors, teachers or revolutionaries, felt impelled to reject their missionary origins. They felt, as so many have felt before them, that Christianity, at least as revealed in the majority of its adherents, was not dynamic enough and, worse, was too solidly on the side of the ruling power. For this the missionaries themselves must bear part of the blame; for too long they have failed to realize how deep is the hurt given by racial arrogance; for too long have they retained to themselves the tit-bits of life, 'because we work so hard, and have given up such a lot'; for too long the lives of some have been lives of sanctified self-indulgence. The attitude of respectable white churchgoers in keeping within their congregations a most strict segregation, 'because we live with these Natives all the week and we do like a bit of time to ourselves at the week-end,' has done untold harm to the cause of Christianity in South Africa which the splendid labours of Scott and Huddleston, Reeves and Clayton have not been powerful enough wholly to neutralize in the minds of thinking Africans.

- The rejection was, then, understandable enough. It was the rejection of the bossiness of the nursery with a final act of rudeness to the departing Nanny, and for the most part has been accepted good humouredly enough, if with a tinge of real pain, by the wiser missionaries. This individual rejection is to be seen as the pattern for the final, national rejection which is the goal towards which, paradoxically, every missionary should have been working. Against this coming time he has been teaching his people, binding them fast to the faith, inculcating in them the confidence that the change is going to need when priest and people alike will be indigenous and the foreign hand be removed. He should not be surprised when the day comes even though it come when he still thinks the people are not ready for it.

Being a mission doctor myself I believe this moment has not been reached in South Africa, but by the close of the century, and possibly before then, it is bound to come. That there has not yet been any very violent reaction is in part due to the kind of work being done by the modern missionary. Nowadays he is unlikely to find himself in the relatively uncomplicated task of direct dissemination of the Gospel. More likely he will be an administrative officer, sharing that work with his priestly function, but as an archdeacon or as a bishop, more preoccupied with the material resources of his diocese than with the cure of individual souls. The work of conversion has passed to his African colleagues, and being less often evident he will be, perhaps, less resented. Yet in a few years he will know that he must decline while his colleagues increase; that he must cease from leadership and become, if he is asked to remain at all, once again a servant, put to work in some corner of the missionary field where, in the opinion of his former junior partners, his talents will be of most use. This is going to be difficult; and there are not many who will look forward with equanimity to this change of roles. He may, in his subordination, remain well aware that he could make a far better job of being the boss than he to whom, for Christ's sake, he has handed the job.

For, in the end, the missionary's job is governed by obedience. By obedience to his calling, to his superiors and to his Master. In so far as he is true to these disciplines he may dare to assume that what he is doing has upon it the seal of God. Through all the folly and self-indulgence, through all the splendour and triumphs of the work, through all the doubts and irritations of his calling, the missionary may hope that God will use his talents and his years to create something good. Even when he stands, his bags packed and labelled, waiting for the train to carry him out of the country of his willing adoption, he may take heart from the knowledge that this too is within the providence of God.

We may, I think, justly pray that we shall see it that way when the time comes.